YUKON GOLD

A GUIDE FOR THE MODERN GOLDSEEKER

Gary Lee

Outcrop the Northern Publishers Ltd.

Design: John Stevenson Rodney Raycroft © Outcrop Ltd.

Editor: Rosemary Allerston

Canadian Cataloguing in Publication Data
Holloway, Samuel D.
Yukon gold

Bibliography: p. 124
Includes index.
ISBN 0-919315-12-7

1. Prospecting — Yukon Territory. 2. Gold — Yukon Territory. I. Title.
TN271.G6H64 1985
622'.3422'097191
C85-091601-1

Outcrop (Yukon) Ltd.
The Northern Publishers
Whitehorse, Yukon

For information, write:
Box 1350, Yellowknife
Northwest Territories
Canada X1A 2N9

Printed and bound in Canada
by John Deyell Company

Cover photo: Richard Hartmier

This book is dedicated to my great-uncle, John J. (Joe) Haley, who trekked to the Klondike in 1894 and lived out his life in the land of gold.

Murdoch's Gem Shop, Whitehorse

All diagrams, maps and photos are by the author, except where noted.

Note: The metric system of weights and measures is not used in this book. Claims are still measured in feet, water in miner's inches, gravel in yards, and gold in troy ounces.

ACKNOWLEDGMENTS

The following people, all of Whitehorse, Yukon, have greatly assisted me in the compilation of this book:

Steve Morrison, Placer Geologist, Exploration and Geological Services, Department of Indian Affairs and Northern Development; George W. Gilbert, Head, Placer Mining Section, Inspector of Mines, DIAND; Rob L. McIntyre, Geology Technician, Manager, Canada Map Office and H.S. Bostock Core Library, DIAND; Dick North, author of *The Mad Trapper of Rat River* and *The Lost Patrol*; Mary Smolders, prospector, proof-reader, typist; Philip Joe, artist. I'm also grateful to Rosemary Allerston, my editor at Outcrop, who shaped the material I compiled into readable form.

Contents

Introduction

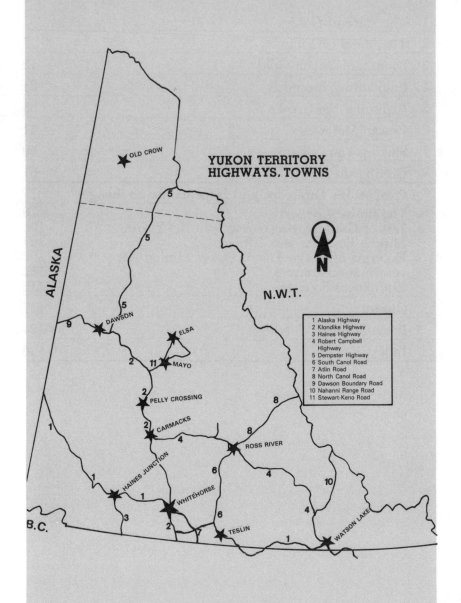

★ OLD CROW

**YUKON TERRITORY
HIGHWAYS, TOWNS**

ALASKA

N.W.T.

5

5

5

9

★ DAWSON

★ ELSA

11 ★ MAYO

2

2

★ PELLY CROSSING

2

★ CARMACKS

4

8

8

★ ROSS RIVER

N

1 Alaska Highway
2 Klondike Highway
3 Haines Highway
4 Robert Campbell
  Highway
5 Dempster Highway
6 South Canol Road
7 Atlin Road
8 North Canol Road
9 Dawson Boundary Road
10 Nahanni Range Road
11 Stewart-Keno Road

1

1

HAINES JUNCTION

6

1

★ WHITEHORSE

4

10

★

1

3

2

6

4

★ TESLIN

1

★ WATSON LAKE

B.C.

INTRODUCTION TO THE YUKON

Yukon Territory, located in the far northwestern corner of Canada, covers an area of 207,076 square miles. It is connected by the Alaska Highway to southern Canada and Alaska, and by the Klondike Highway to Skagway, Alaska, on the Pacific coast. Its northern boundary is the shoreline of the Beaufort Sea. There are major transportation routes to and from Outside, including scheduled jet service. Internal highways connect major centres.

The Yukon is a country of extremes. The subarctic climate is undeniably harsh, and temperatures zigzag widely, from occasional very hot days in summer to frequent very cold ones in winter. It's an adventurous land, a magnet to travelers.

New interest in gold mining for fun as well as profit is bringing many thousands of visitors to the Yukon every year. They're awed and challenged by the magnificent landscape of mountains, lakes and river valleys. They come mostly in summer, the most practical time for many Outsiders, who take advantage of long, glorious hours of sunshine and warm temperatures, to enjoy the country and what it has to offer.

Similarly, summer is the best time for prospecting and mining activities in the Yukon. Cold temperatures keep the streams solid for much of the year, and the mining season can be said to last from the end of May to the end of September, with an allowance of weeks at either end to really stretch things.

Knowledge of these seasonal restrictions is indispensible to prospectors, who should equip themselves accordingly. A few other restrictions apply. For instance, no prospecting or mining is permitted in National Park areas. And remember, much ground you'll encounter will have been staked by others.

It is a serious offence to look for gold on someone else's claim. In most cases it is legal to traverse the claims of others if it is the only route to more distant claims. If a trail or road must be built across another person's claim for mining purposes then an agreement must be reached with that person as to location and size of this road. (See also the chapter on Staking Your Claim.)

Under present mining laws any person of any nationality, legally present in Canda and 18 years of age or older, may stake and record gold claims in the Yukon. To actually *mine* these properties the visitor must obtain a work permit from the Canadian Department of Employment and Immigration, Room 101, Federal Building, Whitehorse, Yukon.

Any miner may import specialized mining equipment from the U.S.A. duty free and federal sales tax-exempt.

DAWSON DAILY NEWS

CANADA'S YUKON POKE POURS GOLD FOR ALL THE WORLD
OUTPUT TO DATE $150,000,000.00

CHAPTER 1

THE LURE OF GOLD

Accursed thirst for gold! What dost thou not compel
mortals to do? *Virgil*

It was gold that opened up the Yukon country, drawing the
Klondikers nearly a century ago. They came in the fabulous Rush
of 1897-8, came by the thousands from almost everywhere and
every walk of life. They were Americans and Canadians,
Englishmen, Orientals, Arabs, Australians, and everything in between.
They were young and old, rich and poor, male and female. They were
farmers and bankers, clergymen and stevedores, clerks and waitresses,
lawyers, storekeepers, confidence men and politicians. They struggled
against horrendous conditions for thousands of miles, through swamps
and torrential river canyons, over glaciers and jagged mountain passes.
Of perhaps a hundred thousand who began the great trek, only about
30,000 made it into the Yukon.

All of them had come for gold.

The word was magic. To the stampeders, the gold fields had the lure
of romance. In a world fast becoming industrialized, here was a fron-
tier to challenge the individual, a free country where you pitted mind,
muscle and heart against the earth itself. And the prize was the sovereign
treasure, gold: the ornament of kings from the beginning of history,
the universal currency against which all others were measured.

There had been other gold rushes in Colorado, California, Australia,
British Columbia. But none surpassed the gold fever of the Klondike.
In a couple of mad years, the treasure hunters built their crazy towns
of tents and log cabins, and scraped the gold valleys bare.

Gold flowed out of the Yukon, many millions of dollars' worth. And with it, after a season or two, went most of the miners.

They left behind a Yukon full of echoes. Reminders of their quest persist today: visitors soak up the atmosphere of Dawson dancehalls and saloons, meticulously restored. They trek to ghost towns in search of memories. And the memories are there. In fact, the Yukon is dotted with rotting cabins and unmarked graves. In the mining areas accessible by road, junk collectors and souvenir hunters have denuded the old camps of their treasures. But if you venture off the regular trails, often for just a few hundred feet, you may stumble upon the remains of an old-timer's abode, untouched since the day he left it; though whether he is buried beside it or managed to get back Outside with a fortune is impossible to tell.

Once, while I was prospecting in an area that had not been mined since about 1910, I found the outline of where a miner's cabin once stood. It had the usual garbage pit beside it, and as I dug through the corned beef tins and coffee cans, I found a bottle that once held Perry Davis' Painkiller, and I found a pair of hobnail boots. The painkiller was a universal remedy in the old days, and you can still buy it in some Northern drugstores. Besides its medicinal properties, the stuff came in handy as a thermometer. At minus 60^0, the liquid turned white; at minus 70^0, it crystallized; and if the temperature sank to 75^0 below zero, Perry Davis' Painkiller froze solid. Finding the bottle in that old dump was a wry link with the past, but the boots affected me more. Their soles were completely worn through, and as I held them I could almost feel the spirit of the man who had worn them for so long.

The spirit of the lone individual inspires many Yukoners today as they search the valleys for gold, often coming across traces of the early miners. Far from their homelands, the old-timers traveled on foot throughout the Yukon, forming tiny settlements on creeks that could be hand mined. Their crude cabins, long since reclaimed by nature, were within hailing distance of one another; the trails they trod with their hobnailed boots are still evident, so hard-packed on the routes from cabins to diggings that no vegetation has yet grown on them.

Although these early placer miners had little knowledge of geology and found their deposits by luck and stubborn work, they did do a thorough job of mining a gold-bearing valley. Rich paystreaks were the only type of ground they could profitably dig; they followed these paystreaks underground with incredible accuracy. Their drifts and adits were hundreds of feet long, often with no shoring, their floors usually covered with water. Working with picks and shovels by candlelight, with no women or children about and no communication with the Outside, the old-timers often stayed on their claims for years before they had gathered a sizable stake or ill-health forced them to leave.

Modern miners are always coming across reminders of the grueling life led by the pioneers, who worked with picks and shovels as their only tools. The old equipment is invariably worn from use: picks are found with only an inch or so of rusty steel stub left.

Such was the lure of gold. And it didn't end with the Gold Rush days. Many miners stayed on for years afterward, and many more came into the country, especially during the Depression years. The land within a few miles of the settlements was pitted with test-holes and shafts. Yet, despite their thorough and unrelenting toil, the early miners did not venture much beyond their little camps. They did not find all the gold there is to be had in the Yukon. Good gold deposits have been found on the fringes of the old camps.

With today's helicopters, all-terrain vehicles, radio telephones, and other mechanized or electronic gadgets, prospectors have an easier time of it. They can profitably work ground that was too poor at $20 or so per ounce of gold. So the quest continues, carried out as always by romantics, adventurers and rugged individualists.

Placer mining is still a way of life for hundreds of Yukoners. In the last five years, 315,493 troy ounces of gold have been exported from the Territory, and large amounts circulate within the local economy.

Many prospectors and geologists believe that much more gold is still in the ground, waiting to be uncovered by modern methods and equipment. Intriguing new theories suggest the presence of buried placer deposits that the old-timers walked over but could not find.

Today's goldseekers have many advantages the stampeders would not have dreamed possible. But looking for gold is still a tough business.

You need to be in good physical condition. The Yukon is still mostly wilderness; its climate and its terrain are harsh. No one should attempt to travel the bush trails or the rivers without expert companionship or thorough experience in the outdoors. You should have an optimistic outlook and the ability to persevere in your search.

And you need a knowledge of basic geology.

This book is intended to provide the fundamentals. Experienced miners will probably find useful information, too, but the intention is to begin at the beginning, and cover everything amateurs need to know. If you're a hobbyist who'd like to spend weekends or holidays following the footsteps of the Klondikers, this book is for you.

Maybe, like myself, you'll fall victim to the incurable lure of the search. My credentials include seven years of part-time goldseeking. I've turned up plenty of colors. I could take you on a panning expedition today and we would find colors in varying amounts all the way from Dawson to Whitehorse. (Colors don't spell riches; they just mean some gold is there.)

4

In Mayo and Dawson they dubbed me the Gold Dust Kid, because I seemed to have the "touch" from the beginning. I pulled a nugget out of the first shovelful of dirt I panned on the Klondike Visitor's Association's recreational claim, much to the astonishment of friends who had dug around all day.

My great uncle Joe Haley, to whom this book is dedicated, trekked to the Klondike in 1894. He struck it rich several times, lost the money in other mining ventures, and died broke. To him, a rich find spoiled the search.

In the philosophies of many old-timers, the thing seems to be the *finding* of the gold, not the gold itself. Robert Service himself put it that way in his poem *Spell of the Yukon*.

I can honestly say it's true of me. Searching for gold could be called a metaphor for something else; it's the quest that counts. In 1983 I stopped mining on a creek because of high rainfall and equipment failures. The following season the same hole yielded 210 ounces – to somebody else. I don't regret the curiosity that led me and a partner to a valley so full of grizzly bears my friend took to shooting all our ammunition in the air, just to relieve the tension. And I don't regret the time I got stuck in a steep-walled canyon when the ice I was walking on gave way, leaving me no way out. (I managed to scale the cliff a day later.)

I've had claims staked from under me by big companies with helicopters, and by prospectors who were smarter than I was, smart enough to stay in one place and not wander off to the next spot. I've damned near drowned in swollen, muddy streams, trying to hook cable around a boulder deep in the muddy water.

You could say, I guess, that I've done most of the things prospectors do. And made most of the mistakes. Along the way, I've picked up the knowledge of the Yukon and its gold creeks I wish I'd had when I began.

This volume is designed to be a primary guide for all those who dream of sharing the adventure Yukon gold represents. No promises are made; you'll have to find the gold on your own. But the facts you'll find here, compiled for the first time for modern goldseekers in the Yukon, are the key to where and how to look.

You don't need a lot of capital, and you don't need experience. You *do* need to do your homework. You need to enjoy the outdoors. And you need a certain amount of determination to master the basics of the placer miner's craft. After that, you're on your way!

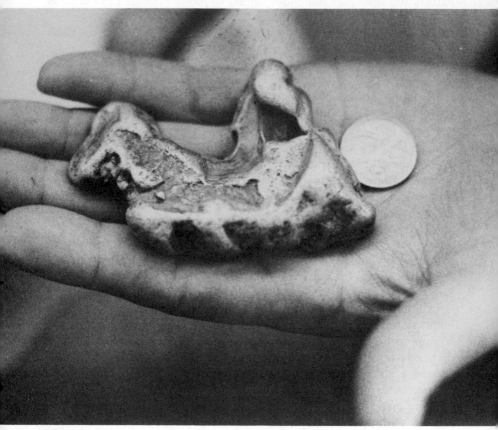

Whitehorse Star

6

CHAPTER 2

THE METAL
OF KINGS

O f the many thousands of goldseekers who flooded the Klondike during the great Rush of '97-'98, only a fraction actually found gold, and of these very few became truly rich. For most, the supreme experience was the rush itself, and the freewheeling spectacle of Dawson in its glory days. A lot of stampeders spent far more money than they ever found, and the vast majority went back home without panning a pinch of dust.

The fact was that too many Klondikers were equipped with little more than their dreams. Few knew where to look for gold, or anything about what geological conditions favor the formation of gold deposits. When it came right down to it, most had no idea what raw gold looks like.

Some arrived in the stampede city expecting to find gold growing from trees, and not a few were certain it would be found in the streets. If these greenhorns were an extreme minority, it was nevertheless true that most who survived the trail were totally ignorant of what to expect. Some would not have recognized gold if they did come across it in the creeks they had come so far to mine.

The Klondikers weren't much different from most of us. Gold, to many, means the shiny, refined metal in jewelry or coins. The bright yellow color and smooth, light-reflecting surface are unmistakable.

But nature's gold is seldom of this purity, so it isn't always easy to recognize. It's almost always *alloyed* with such metals as silver or copper.

This fusing affects the yellow color: it can be very pale if the proportion of silver in the alloy is high; or reddish-looking if heavily mixed with copper.

The gleam of gold can be dulled by chemical processes affecting the minerals it's associated with. Sometimes, for example, its appearance is dark and rusty, if it's coated with iron oxide. Or it can look black if coated with manganese.

In addition, raw gold takes many forms. It's found in grains as fine as flour; as flakes, scales, or wires; and as nuggets of various sizes. Sometimes it even takes crystalline forms. It may be embedded in solid rock as part of a vein or lode; or mixed with loose sand and gravel.

To further complicate matters, some other minerals look a lot like gold. "Fool's gold" glitters just like the real thing in the eager eyes of the greedy or over-hasty. Such was the embarrassing experience of Elizabethan explorer Martin Frobisher, who triumphantly bore 16 shiploads of gold "ure" all the way from Baffin Island to London, before an expert pointed out that the glittery stuff wasn't really gold at all. Countless others have made similar mistakes, if on a more modest scale.

Pyrites are among the less valuable minerals frequently confused with gold; they have a very similar, gleaming-yellow color. To distinguish gold from look-alikes, you have to be familiar with its other properties.

Properties of gold

Gold is an *element*, a substance occurring in nature which can't be broken down by ordinary chemical means into different substances. (Elements can be transformed into other *elements* by extraordinary means: radioactive decay or nuclear reactions. But that's beyond the scope of this book!)

Gold is a *noble* metal, which means it's an inert substance, unaffected by most chemicals and acids, though a few will dissolve it. But it won't, for example, corrode in air or sea water, so it's extremely durable. Pirate bullion emerges from hundreds of years of submersion as shiny as the day it sank; surgical implants are unaffected by (and don't affect) human tissue; and gold teeth outlast the head that holds them. Gold rings manufactured today may be made from metal actually mined in ancient Rome, perhaps used and melted down many times over the centuries.

Gold is an excellent conductor of electricity; it's also very *ductile*, which means it can be stretched almost unimaginably thin. Tiny threads are used for complicated circuitry in microchips so small they're almost invisible. It can be used as the skin of a satellite or as a film on office windows that conserves energy. (A cubic inch of gold can be hammered into a sheet that would cover 16,000 square inches!)

8

Tests for gold

It's easy to use your knowledge of gold's properties to distinguish it from such look-alikes as pyrites. The following simple tests can be done with a sample of the mineral you're trying to identify. By comparing the properties revealed with the Mineralogy Table, you'll soon be able to tell whether what you've found is the real thing, or just another lump of "fool's gold."

Test 1: Rub the mineral on *unglazed* porcelain. A streak of color will be left. The chart describes the streaks left by gold and by its look-alike minerals.

Test 2: Scratch the sample to test its *hardness*. Resistance to scratching is expressed on a scale from 1 to 10. Window glass, for example, has a hardness of 5.5. Your own fingernail is about 1.5. The chart gives figures for the various minerals you might be examining.

Test 3: Determine the *specific gravity* of the mineral by weighing a sample, then immersing it in a measuring cup of water and weighing the water the sample has displaced. If the specimen weighs 3 times as much as the displaced water, it has a specific gravity of 3. Use the chart to find which minerals have the specific gravity you've obtained with the water test.

Mineralogy Table

Mineral	Hardness	Specific Gravity	Characteristics
gold	2.5 – 3	19.3	Color, yellow; streak, yellow; malleable; commonly in flakes, nuggets, scales, or wires, reflects light equally in all directions.
chalcopyrite	3.5	4.2	Color, brass-yellow; streak, greenish black; very brittle; surface could have blue or green areas since it is about 34% copper.
pyrrhotite	3.5 – 4	4.5	Color, bronze-yellow; streak, grey-black; tarnishes easily; slightly magnetic.
pyrite	6 – 6.5	5	Color, brass-yellow; streak, greenish black; alters to brown limonite (rust).
marcasite	6 – 6.5	4.9	Color, pale yellow; streak, greyish to brownish black; alters to limonite or to iron sulfates.

Its softness makes gold a traditional material for jewelry. It can take on the shapes imagined by the jeweler, whether filligreed or sculpted, and will not shatter under the stresses of the work. This workable softness and its eternal luster give gold the classification of *precious metal*. In turn, the fact that it's so sought-after makes gold an ideal standard of international exchange. Gold has become synonymous with wealth throughout the world.

Troy Weights		
24 grains	=	1 pennyweight
20 pennyweights	=	1 ounce (oz t.)
12 ounces	=	1 pound (lb t.)
1 troy pound	=	.3229 avoirdupois pound
1 troy ounce	=	1.0971 avoirdupois ounce
1 grain	=	64.7989 mg (metric)

How pure is it?

In commercial gold production, gold must be removed from source gravels or rock (the mining process); then it must be *refined*. This is necessary to remove all impurities, or to break down alloys with copper or silver.

Some gold found in Yukon creeks can be as high as 98% pure, but most is of a lower grade, down to about 65% pure. Prices drop accordingly, except for nuggets interesting enough to be used as jewelry. Purity can vary within the same district and even on the same creek.

Gold is generally described in terms of its *fineness*, on a scale of parts per thousand. Pure gold is designated *1,000 fine*. Gold classified 921 fine would contain 921 parts per thousand of gold, 79 parts per thousand of other metals.

(Jewelers use their own terminology. A pure gold ring is 24 karat gold. Since such a ring is very soft, an alloy with copper or silver is more common, and its purity would be rated at 18, 14, or 10 karats.)

Experienced goldseekers find they can often judge the purity of crude gold by its appearance. The color will be light if a sample is heavily alloyed with silver; or the luster may be reduced. Gold which has been broken down by the action of water to very small particles – *flour gold* or "dust" as the old-timers called it – is often very pure, which accounts for the trouble people take to recover it.

Murdoch's Gem Shop, Whitehorse

Yukon Archives

CHAPTER 3

SOURCES OF YUKON GOLD

Finding gold in the Yukon isn't a matter of blind luck, though many of the Klondike stampeders undoubtedly thought so. The eagerness with which so many thousands of them came pouring into the country in '97 and '98 is evidence of the illogic, superstition, and tireless hope of the human species: the hectic bonanza years fulfilled the dreams of very few.

Yet, there *was* gold. Perhaps 4,000 Klondikers found it, and a few of these found incomparable riches: $5.6 million dollars came out of Bonanza and Eldorado Creeks alone during the first year of the rush – and this when gold was priced at under $20 an ounce! In the decade at the turn of the century, $100 million in gold was mined, and production has continued ever since.

In fact, the best sites have been worked repeatedly since the stampede. Big companies with large-scale machinery took over from the Klondikers, and the fabled creeks were mined again by both big and small operators during the "new gold rush" of the 1970s, when gold prices reached all-time high levels.

Where to look for Yukon gold

While this book advises that it's a good *general* rule for amateur goldseekers to go where gold has been found before, it's obvious that

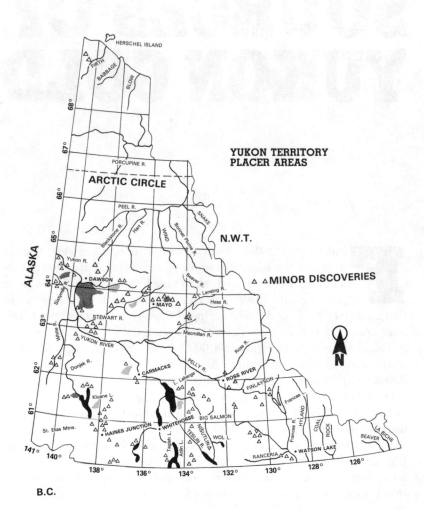

HERSCHEL ISLAND

FIRTH
BABBAGE
BLOW

68°
67°

PORCUPINE R.

ARCTIC CIRCLE

66°

PEEL R.

65°

Blackstone R.
Hart R.
WIND
Bonnet Plume R.
SNAKE

YUKON TERRITORY
PLACER AREAS

N.W.T.

ALASKA

64°

Yukon R.
DAWSON
Stewart R.
White R.

Beaver R.
Lansing R.
MAYO
Hess R.

△ △ MINOR DISCOVERIES

63°

STEWART R.
YUKON RIVER

Macmillan R.

62°

Donjek R.
CARMACKS
PELLY R.
Ross R.

N

61°

Kluane L.
ROSS RIVER
L. Laberge
FINLAYSON
Frances L.

St. Elias Mtns.
HAINES JUNCTION
WHITEHORSE
BIG SALMON
NISUTLIN R.
WOL L.
HYLAND
COAL
ROCK
LA BICHE
BEAVER

141°
140°

Tagish L.
Atlin L.
TESLIN R.
RANCERIA
Frances R.
WATSON LAKE

138°
136°
134°
132°
130°
128°
126°

B.C.

14

sites which have been scoured repeatedly by others must be approached with proven methods, not wishful thinking.

The same is true if you hope to discover new deposits of gold or to strike out into territory you think others may have worked only lightly.

You need to base your activities on a sound understanding of the geological processes that result in deposits of gold. Combined with the proven methods outlined in these pages, your knowledge can mean success where many others have failed.

Yukon gold is placer gold

The electrifying discoveries that set off the Klondike rush were made by independent prospectors using simple hand methods. Anyone, it seemed, could do the same. And so began history's greatest case of gold fever.

Not that the experience was entirely new. The California gold rush of 1849 was still fresh in the minds of the stampeders who fought their way into the Yukon in '97-'98. Despite the difference in climate, there was a good deal of similarity between the two settings. Both California and the Yukon lured many thousands – people from all walks of life, each and every one convinced that a share in the bonanza awaited him. All you needed was energy, fired by dreams of instant wealth, and one or two inexpensive tools

These romantic assumptions were at least partly true. California's gold, like that of the Yukon, could actually be retrieved by hand, using equipment that required minimal investment. The individual had a chance in those days, and still does today.

Why? Because much of the gold in these regions is found in *placers*.

Placers are deposits of sand, gravel, or other material that contain a recoverable amount of gold or valuable minerals. These heavy minerals have been accumulated by natural mechanical processes and the exploitation of these loose, drifted minerals is called *placer mining*. (The word, pronounced with a short "a" as in *apple*, is derived from the Spanish *placel* which means "sandbank.")

The loose, unconsolidated material that hosts placer gold is really broken-down rock and fragments of minerals, although these may be well rounded by the action of running water and abrasion. There are mineral deposits remaining in place in the solid rock of the Yukon, of course. These *lodes* must be mined by *hardrock* or *quartz* methods, which require equipment and cash investment far beyond the scope of the small operator, and therefore of this book.

Here we're concerned only with placer mining. It's the one mining operation that can be carried out by individuals, using simple, inexpensive equipment.

15

Much of the gold in placers takes the form of fine grains – the "dust" you hear so much about in accounts of the California and Klondike gold rushes. The age-long process by which gold is freed from host rock and deposited great distances away causes the breakdown to small particles.

Still, larger pieces of gold constantly occur. They range from *coarse* gold to nuggets, and are classified in a specific way:

Classification of Placer Gold

Nuggets	1mm or larger	up to 200 per troy ounce
Coarse	10 mesh*	up to 500 per troy ounce
Medium	10 to 20 mesh	up to 2,000 per troy ounce
Fine	20 to 40 mesh	up to 12,000 per troy ounce
Very fine	40 mesh	up to 40,000 per troy ounce
Flour gold		dust

Mesh refers to the number of openings per square inch in a wire screen.

Most gold in placer deposits is irregularly shaped, and worn by the action of water and friction. It's also of varying degrees of purity, never more than 980 fine.

How placers are formed

Geologists explain placers in terms of very ancient, large-scale earth processes. It's useful to outline these, because the better you understand them, the better a prospector you'll be.

If you look at a relief map of North America, you can trace the huge mountain chains that run down the Western side of the continent. This *Cordilleran* region is composed of the Sierras, Cascades, Rockies and other chains, from Mexico to Alaska. Gold discoveries have frequently been made all along the Cordillera, in New Mexico, Nevada, Colorado, Montana, Idaho, Washington, British Columbia and Alaska, as well as California and the Yukon.

The pattern of these gold deposits relates to the forming of the mountain ranges.

The earth's crust has shifted and changed many times over the billions of years since the planet was formed. The rock layers of the earth's crust have been pushed, folded and cracked repeatedly. The continents themselves have drifted. Within them, seas have flooded and retreated, mountain ranges have risen and sunk, forests have flourished and died.

Over millions of years, the vast changes in the planet's surface layers caused rock types to mix and fuse; huge fissures permitted molten materials from the depths to rise to the upper layers.

Among these was the element gold, which flowed as a hot liquid into cracks in the crust, where it cooled and hardened. Such deposits are called *veins*.

In regions of the continent which have been relatively unaffected by heaving and buckling, very ancient rocks lie at the surface. One such region, the Canadian Shield, is the site of a good deal of mining activity today. The Shield has been relatively flat for many millions of years, and its veins of minerals have remained in place.

If, however, the Shield's ancient Precambrian rock had been thrust upward to form mountain ranges, the story might have been different. It might have resembled what occurred in the jagged regions of the Western Cordillera.

The processes in the life of mountains are continuous. Once these high projections of the rocky crust are thrust above sea level, the forces of wind and water begin, slowly and relentlessly, to wear them down to sea level once more.

Erosion of land occurs in three stages. In the earliest, the *youth* stage, the mountains are at their highest elevation. Rain falls on the peaks; streams form and cut sharply downward. The relentless action of the water wears away the rock, carrying off the debris of gradual breakage. The flowing water seeks the lowest possible level, and there it deposits the debris in steep mountain clefts, which become river valleys in the land's *maturity* stage.

Wind, frost, and chemical action aid the weathering process.

Over many millions of years, as weathering breaks down high-level rock, it releases minerals from their veins and from the rock itself. The debris tumbles from high ground to low, eventually finding its way to the bottoms of the streams that etch the valley floors.

Since it is heavier than the gravels carried down with it, gold accumulates at this lowest level, while gravels are swept along by the moving water.

Other heavy minerals may accumulate along with the gold: silver, platinum, hematite, magnetite. Even this mixture may be slowly carried downstream unless it's caught by obstructions in the bedrock.

The process is repeated again and again. Debris from landslides and various other sources sloughs down the valley and into the stream bed.

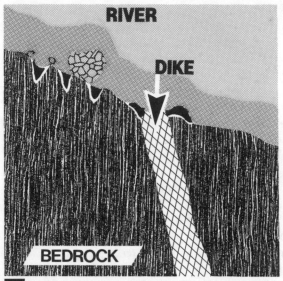

Placer deposits in bedrock crevices, behind and under boulders, and around dikes (pillars of harder rock), in the river bottom.

The valleys widen as the mountains are worn down. As the land enters its *old age*, placers may become deeply buried.

Placers are generally *unconsolidated* deposits (loose fragments), but may sometimes be found in *conglomerate* from an earlier geological age. (Conglomerates are cemented gravels.) Buried placers may be re-elevated by disturbances of the earth's crust. The whole cycle, in fact, begins again.

The natural forces that deposit gold in stream beds can be summarized this way: gold is eroded from its original host rock and is carried downward to the bottoms of streams at the lowest elevations. In streams it shows patterns of accumulation; prospectors rely on such patterns to find placer gold.

Patterns of placer deposits

Relatively heavy placers usually lie on bedrock. Gold tends to stop on the downstream side of natural ridges in the bedrock, or on the insides of bends in the stream or where the bedrock is elevated so as to slow up or widen a stream. (Sometimes the deposit will lie on a "false bedrock" of clay or other tightly packed material above the true bedrock.) This *paystreak*, as it is called, will often be quite narrow as it meanders through a valley and sometimes may disappear altogether. The rest of the valley may also contain placer gold but this material will not be as rich as the primary paystreak.

Generally speaking, the coarsest gold is found in the upper reaches of a stream, while finer-grained gold tends to be deposited in the lower

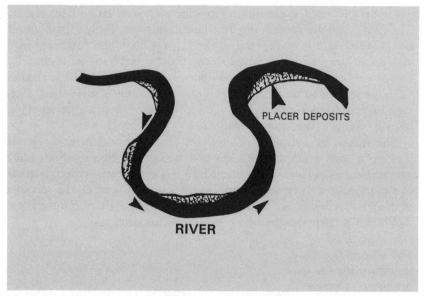

PLACER DEPOSITS

RIVER

Placer deposits in a meandering river

portions of the stream valley. Larger nuggets occur among coarse gravels; fine-grained gold is found with fine, sandy sediments.

Gold found on bedrock with a steep slope is coarser than gold found on a more level bottom. Gold which has washed into narrow canyons or gulches will be coarser than gold found in other locations.

Sometimes a river or creek will change course or downcut quickly, leaving its old channel above the present stream banks. Placers contained in these old channels are called *bench placers*.

In other cases a glacier may scour an area of its placers and move them to a new location. Subsequent stream action may then form a new placer by re-concentrating the gold contained in the glacial material.

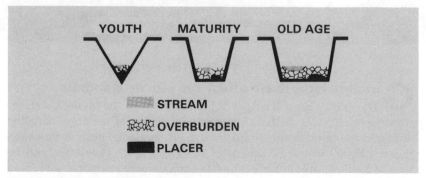

YOUTH   MATURITY   OLD AGE

STREAM
OVERBURDEN
PLACER

The formation of a paystreak in a valley

Gravel-plain placers are found in wide valleys or on alluvial plains. The gold is usually moderately fine and evenly distributed throughout the gravels. As a slow-moving stream moves back and forth across a valley, the meander bends tend to move downstream, so that eventually the whole valley bottom is acted upon by the water. Gold is eroded from the stream banks and a great amount of material is washed. This type of deposit can also occur in a wide valley when a swift-moving stream changes course frequently.

The richest gravel-plain placers are usually found in unglaciated regions; a good example being the lower Klondike River valley. They can also occur in river valleys that have been downcut through areas of older glacial debris; an example of this can be found on the terraces of the Stewart River. So far, the only economical means of mining these deposits has been the use of huge bucket-line dredges.

Three conditions are necessary for the formation of a placer:

1. The presence of gold in deposits, veins or the surrounding rock.
2. A long period of weathering and chemical decomposition to allow the gold to separate from the surrounding rock.
3. Concentration of the gold, usually by water.

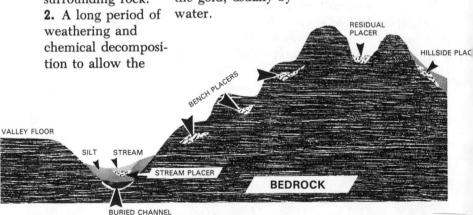

Types of placer deposits

Glaciers and their effect on placer deposits

The earth's great Ice Ages did much to shape the planet's surface. As ancient climates shifted, huge, moving layers of ice crept over the land and retreated again – four times in all, in glacial periods that each lasted 100,000 years. Remnants of the gigantic ice sheets can still be seen in high mountain ranges and in cold northern regions, including the Yukon.

20

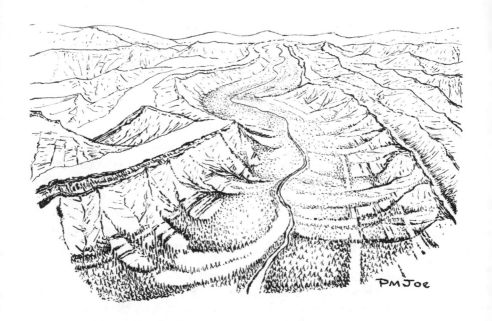

A glaciated valley

The ice sheets were formed by powerful natural forces. They began in northern winters, when more snow fell than could melt in summer. Slowly, successive layers of snow compacted into great masses of ice, whose sheer weight caused lower layers to begin a plastic flow.

These huge, moving layers of ice were up to two miles thick and covered much of the Northern Hemisphere. The northwestern Yukon and some parts of Alaska were somehow unglaciated; it's thought that the high St. Elias mountain range prevented moisture-laden clouds from reaching these areas.

In the western mountains of North America, most glaciers moved down into existing valleys, which became *glacial troughs*. These valley glaciers sometimes joined in a continuous mass of ice and formed *continental glaciers*.

Valley glaciers can still be seen today. They erode their troughs in several ways: the ice flows around rock fragments and carries these away; or the moving ice plucks up chunks of bedrock, some of which become embedded in the *sole* (underbelly) of the glacier. The ice continues to move, scouring the valley; the rocks frozen into the sole produce scratches *(striations)* in the direction of flow. These striations can often be distinctly seen from the air.

Glaciated valleys usually have a fairly flat grade that steepens sharply at the valley head, where the glacier may form a *cirque*. Sometimes likened to an amphitheatre, the cirque is caused when ice freezes into

21

cracks around rocks and plucks them away to form a semi-circular basin.

The sides of glaciated valleys are sheared off, forming steep walls; their most recognizable characteristic is the U-shaped cross-section cut out by the ice. Creeks entering the main valley usually enter at a high level, often forming a waterfall. The flow-courses of these high-level creeks are called *hanging valleys*.

Effects of glaciers on the land surface

The front of a moving glacier acts like a huge plow, slowly pushing up a mass of material in front of it. When glacial motion stops and the ice retreats, this wall of material is left piled up in a *push moraine*. A *terminal moraine* is the mass of material left at the lower end of a glacier after it melts. Both of these moraines are sometimes called *end moraines*. All of the unconsolidated material that originates from glaciation is called *glacial drift* and this material is further classified into two types.

Till (unstratified drift) consists of material of various sizes, from large boulders down to the finest of particles. This is all jumbled together with no pattern of layers. Till can be recognized by the occurence of boulders and tiny clay particles in the same deposit, and by the presence of rocks from outside the drainage area. *Ground moraine*, another form of till, is the material left on the ground after the glacier melts. Although usually occurring in a thin layer, this cover may also be hundreds of feet thick.

Till-covered areas usually have a rough surface, and huge boulders may dot the landscape. Sometimes these boulders are left perched on hillsides; being unstable, they topple down into the valleys.

When a block of glacial ice which is surrounded by drift melts, it leaves a depression in the surface called a *kettle*. Lakes found in these small, closed basins are called *kettle lakes*.

Stratified drift is deposited as glacial outwash by streams and at times is hard to distinguish from other water-laid sediments. This material was sometimes carried many miles past the original extent of the glacier by the water from the melting of this glacier. *Eskers* are a familiar form of stratified drift; they are long ridges formed by streams which flowed under the ice.

Glaciers and gold

Some placer deposits were formed before the glacial epochs, during the Tertiary period of geological time. The Klondike valleys were never glaciated: the placers there were fabulously rich and ridiculously easy to find. This may have influenced early theorists, who advised placer prospectors to stay away from areas that had been ice-covered. It was thought that the placers were likely to have been scattered by the ice and lost forever. This assumption has since proven to be incorrect: most of the placers found in the province of British Columbia are in glaciated terrain. In the Yukon about 10 percent of placer gold production comes from these areas. The Livingstone (Salmon River) goldfields were glaciated at least three times, yet have produced thousands of ounces of gold.

There are several theories about why placers sometimes occur in glaciated areas:

1. Mountainous terrain was not uniformly scoured by the ice.

2. If the ice crossed certain creek valleys at right angles, their placer deposits would be protected.

3. Very deep channels were not affected.

4. Some valleys were only slightly glaciated; these usually do not have cirques at their heads.

5. Placers were formed during interglacial periods and escaped being destroyed by later glaciation, since later glaciers did not advance as far as the early ones. The effects on a valley of the most recent glacial advance can be observed: among them would be sheer valley walls and hanging valleys. But the work of previous glaciers is not so easily detected. The reworking of material released by older glaciers would have been greatly assisted by tremendous amounts of melt-water as the latest glacier was melting. Much of the gold discovered in glaciated valleys is coarse and uniform in size, as if sorted by powerful streams.

6. Placers may have formed in the streams that ran alongside retreating ice sheets. These side channels were deeply cut in a relatively short time, and usually filled later with outwash or recent deposits. Some streams fed by the melting of great masses of ice have since disappeared; placers they formed may be far away from present day water-courses.

7. New placers may have formed after the retreat of the last glaciers. When a glacier scoured out a valley to produce the characteristic U-shape, any placers in the valley would be incorporated into the glacial till, probably in the end moraine. The large volumes of water from melting ice would act to sort the debris and reconcentrate the placers.

In general, it's safe to say that in mountainous terrain, areas once glacier-covered offer good potential for undiscovered placers. Other factors must also be present.

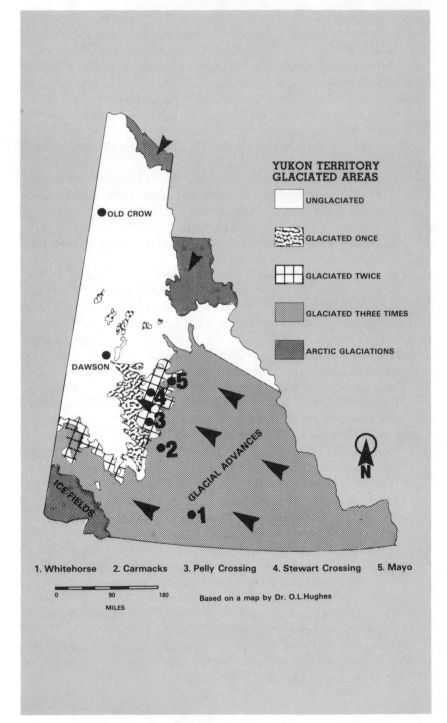

YUKON TERRITORY
GLACIATED AREAS

UNGLACIATED

GLACIATED ONCE

GLACIATED TWICE

GLACIATED THREE TIMES

ARCTIC GLACIATIONS

OLD CROW

DAWSON

GLACIAL ADVANCES

ICE FIELDS

N

1. Whitehorse   2. Carmacks   3. Pelly Crossing   4. Stewart Crossing   5. Mayo

0   90   180
MILES

Based on a map by Dr. O.L.Hughes

24

The prospector must be able to imagine what the land looked like before any glaciation took place, and to visualize the changes wrought by successive stages of glaciation. The effects of advancing and retreating ice must be considered, as well as those of the tremendous runoffs of glacial melt-water. Small, V-shaped valleys bordered by rock benches probably offer the best potential sites for original placers.

Aerial photographs may help prospectors locate former stream beds, but many of these channels are likely to be covered by drift. Some smaller valleys may be completely filled in.

Drift mining has been the most successful method of placer mining in glaciated areas. The miner must be prepared to deal with large boulders and inconsistent paystreaks.

The map shows the valleys in the Yukon where placers are known to be located. Some of these finds have been legendary gold-producers. It's worth a glance backward at one of the most famous, Bonanza Creek.

The historic Bonanza Creek placers

Prospectors who staked the first significant finds at Bonanza Creek found themselves in a narrow valley, bordered by gently curving hills sloping upward towards King Solomon's Dome. The hillsides were lush with vegetation and the valley where the creek ran was a dense tangle of jackpine, spruce and birch forest.

Coarse gold was discovered right in the surface gravels of the creek, and when the first claims were recorded, the wild stampede began. Bonanza Creek and its tributary, Eldorado, were soon swarming with prospectors.

Tales were carried to the outside world, each one more fantastic than the last. One man found 3½ ounces of gold in a single panful of dirt; another miner gleaned 12½ ounces from one pan. These finds were completely outclassed when a prospector found 50 ounces in a pan, and even this was topped in 1899, when a single panful of gravel yielded an incredible 62½ ounces of gold.

Stories of such finds were a siren lure. Trekkers from all over North America and Europe, and even from Australia and China, rushed helter skelter into the Yukon.

And the discoveries at Bonanza Creek continued. Six-ounce nuggets were commonplace, scarcely noticed by the hardened hands. One man working on a fraction (an under-sized claim) was able to recover 240 troy *pounds* of gold in an eight-hour shift. (Had this happened in 1980 he would have made $2,448,000 as a short day's pay.) In the Klondike summer the sun shone almost around the clock, and along the valleys piles of dirt thrown out on the surface showed their gleaming treasures to all who passed by.

Yukon Archives

26

Hand mining of the creeks continued for the next four years and each claim on Bonanza and Eldorado Creeks yielded over 6,000 troy pounds of gold, worth about $20,000,000 per claim at today's prices. The benches above the creeks produced some 2,600 troy pounds of gold per bench claim.

Mechanized mining methods and hydraulicking of the hillsides began taking over from the hand methods. These operations continued to wrest gold from the Klondike for another 65 years. Over the last decade the gravels have again been re-worked. It seems that the valleys and benches will continue to produce gold, though the average yield per yard is becoming steadily smaller.

But once in a while a hint of old-time Klondike paydirt turns up. In 1977, a miner on Hunker Creek recovered 70 ounces of gold from one quarter-yard section of gravel. In 1963, a lone miner with a rocker gleaned 50 ounces of gold from a small area where Seven Pup Creek enters Victoria Gulch.

Obviously these were pockets the old-timers missed.

It is not likely that there is still an undiscovered placer field the size of the Klondike discovery. There is a good chance, however, of there being smaller, very rich placers in isolated creek valleys or in old dry channels away from the present water-courses.

In the western part of the Territory between latitude 63 00' N and latitude 63 15' N, a new placer field was discovered in 1974 by geologist M. Kenyon. He found coarse, easy-to-pan gold in the upper reaches of a creek which flows out a small mountain chain called the Moosehorn Range. Test pitting along this creek (since named Kenyon Creek) revealed no less than one-half ounce of gold per yard of gravel. Coarse, plentiful gold was also discovered on other creeks in the same area.

This find suggests that good research plus a solid grasp of the principles of placer gold deposition can pay off handsomely. This may well be true anywhere in the Yukon, whether on well-beaten paths, or in remote river valleys.

Most goldseekers rely on the accepted theory of placer formation. But an increasing number are investigating new angles.

We've explained that gold contained in placers has been released from lode deposits or veins by erosion. But no mother lode has ever been found in any of the major placer areas of the Yukon.

In addition, some finds of placer gold don't seem to fit the prevailing theory of deposition. Old-time prospectors have believed for many years that gold can "grow." How else, they reason, can you explain why good-sized nuggets are sometimes found in very unlikely places? In 1983 Queenstake Resources discovered a round pebble of tin oxide and quartz with a gold nugget attached to it. In the words of geologist Angus Woodsend, "It was the equivalent of a peach growing on an apple tree." Another anomaly turned up on Miller Creek in 1982 – a gold-plated nail from an old sluice box.

Geologist R. G. McConnell came across another curiosity:

> The gold on Miller and Glacier Creeks is derived, in large measure, directly from the quartz veins and silicified schists of the district, but some evidence was obtained in the course of the exploration, serving to show that some of it has been deposited from solution. A boulder was found in one of the workings on Miller Creek, the upper surface of which was partially covered with specks and scales of crystalline gold. The crystals were arranged in dendritic forms, and while some of them were firmly attached to the rock, others separated easily from it. The angles of the crystals were sharp and showed no wear of any kind, while the boulder itself, an autoclastic quartz-mica schist, was well rounded. The gold evidently did not belong to the rock originally, and the only explanation of its occurrence under the peculiar conditions stated, seems to be that it was taken up by some solvent and redeposited on the surface of the boulder in the position in which it was found. A number of specimens of unworn crystalline gold in filiform and dendritic shapes have been found on Eldorado and other Klondike creeks, which were probably formed in the same way, although no direct evidence of this has hitherto been obtained. (Reprinted from the *Bostock Report*, by permission of Supply and Services Canada.)

There's still a lot of head-scratching over seeming variations in the process of placer deposition. Sourdoughs and professional geologists alike have their theories.

In 1982, Dr. Dirk Tempelman-Kluit, of the Department of Indian Affairs and Northern Development's geological services division in Whitehorse, wrote a paper entitled "White Channel Gravels of the Klondike," in which he puts forth an argument for a groundwater theory of gold deposition. Tempelman-Kluit speculates that circulating acid groundwater dissolves gold from bedrock and from the overlying gravels, then precipitates it at the interface between these two. Such a groundwater system might also produce lode deposits of gold in fractures in the bedrock.

The areas most favorable to such gold deposits would lie in Klondike Schist terrain (See Geological Survey of Canada Map No. 1505A). This terrain carries many narrow quartz veins containing minor traces of gold and the bedrock is fairly soft and foliated. The Klondike and Livingstone gold fields both lie within these zones.

Tempelman-Kluit also suggests some favorable sites for ground-water precipitation of gold to occur, naming some of the left-limit tributaries of the White River, such as Kennebec, Caledonia, and O'Brien Creeks.

The main implications of Tempelman-Kluit's theory can be summed up this way:

1. No high-grade lode source would be necessary to produce these gold deposits.

2. Gold could be "growing" in gravels elsewhere, even in creek valleys from which there has been no known production.

3. Since the groundwater process would have been at work below the surface, these deposits might be far enough down so that they could not be detected by the standard means of prospecting; that is, with a shovel and pan.

If this or any other new theory of gold deposition is proven, the possibility is strong that there are many untapped gold sources in the Yukon.

The question can't be ignored, either by prospectors eager to try out new theories, or by established mining interests.

The staff of the exploration and geological services division of the federal government's Whitehorse offices are diligently pursuing the problem. Since placer geologist Steve Morison joined the staff in 1982, several new possibilities have been investigated.

Morison is the author of a forthcoming paper, *Placer Deposits of Canada*, to be published by Supply and Services Canada. I'm indebted to him for much of the technical information in this book. The reports of this department are closely studied and acted upon by mining companies and individuals.

The entire mining industry in the Yukon has a big stake in the problem, since hardrock and placer mining operations are governed by different sets of regulations. What if the two types can't be distinguished? If placer gold doesn't originate on eroding hillsides, but in the creek beds themselves – by a process we don't yet understand – what becomes of the legal rights of placer operators? Klondike placer miners traditionally went beyond sifting creek gravels: they often dug right into the bedrock, sometimes as far down as 12 feet. If the gold they found trapped in the bedrock were to be classified as lode gold, they may not have been mining legally at all.

To cover their bets, some mining companies have recently staked large tracts of hardrock claims over placer areas – just in case the gold there has "grown" by some yet-to-be-discovered natural means.

Dawson Daily News

DAWSON
YUKON TERRITORY
JULY 21, 1909

DAWSON CITY, YUKON TERRITORY.

DAWSON

(Written Specially for the Dawson News.)

(By ROBERT W. SERVICE, Author of Songs of a Sourdough and Ballads of a Cheechaco.)

FROM the heart of the Frozen Twilight the strong land spake her sons:
"Long are my valleys silent—seek them, ye fearless ones;
Haste, oh men of my measure! Richly the treasure runs."

Then up river and valley streamed the host of the brave;
Then with on-rush and rally flooded the human wave.
er-a-one was weakling; fiercely they took and gave.

ed they the creeks asunder, routed hardship and pain;
a down-laden with plunder, weary from stress and strain.
to death of the battle, came into camp again.

There on the flat by the Yukon, ringed by inviolate snows,
Care-free and comely to look on, gold-born the city arose,
City of homes and hearth-fires the heart of the Northman knows.

He spends of the valley's treasure in all the ports o' the sea;
Far in the chase of pleasure he ranges eager and free;
Yet aye to the Gold-born City the love of his heart must be.

City the sun rejoices, skies of midnight aglow,
Babble of childish voices, gardens where poppies blow,
Cabins with curtained windows, snugly nestling low.

Yea, though the stress be over, the Land hath its treasure still.
Dream of it, world-wide rover, the old town under the hill;
Blue at its feet the river, skies opalescent above,
Homes and gardens and children, peace and plenty and love.

CHAPTER 4

PINPOINTING PROSPECTS

Research is the first and most important tool of the successful goldseeker. The opportunities available are covered in the following pages. Take full advantage of them, beginning before you set out to actually explore. Prospecting in old files and archives is a fascinating pursuit any time, and many goldseekers joyfully indulge themselves over long winter months when they can't be in the field.

I've tried to include some of the best material right here in this book, but that only scratches the surface. Make it your business to read everything you can get your hands on, especially current publications by mining companies and geological agencies.

Many valuable periodicals are now defunct. One of the most colorful of these, *The Placer Mining Times*, was published only from June to November, 1983. If you can dig up copies, you'll find a lively debate of miners versus government regulation, a reflection of the consciousness of the 1980s. (Note: As we go to press, *The Placer Mining Times* is once more being published).

An instructive contrast can be observed in old periodicals from more freewheeling days. I discovered an example of such a newspaper in a Gold Rush era house in Dawson. *The Dawson Daily News Special Edition* of July 21, 1909 was an unabashed promotion by government of the Yukon in general and the mining industry in particular. It was full of glowing testimonials, extravagant predictions and – most important to a prospector today – detailed accounts of work being done on the various local creeks. The *Daily News* outlasted its rivals, publishing until 1954. Archival and library copies are worthwhile reading to the goldseeker.

Maps: your first source of information

Remember: always check claim maps on an area (available at mining recorders' offices) before you pick a site for exploration. If you want to find co-ordinates for any creek or river not on this book's list (page 100), or for that matter, co-ordinates of any named place in the Yukon: towns, lakes, rivers, mountains, see the *Gazeteer of Canada: Yukon Territory*.

Treasure maps, available from Yukon mining recorders, are also extremely important sources of information on gold-bearing regions. It's well worth getting copies. Map and reference sources are listed on pages 33 and 112 of this book.

Topographic maps

These maps show the "lay of the land." Such features as lakes, rivers, creeks, highways and towns are shown, with their height above sea level. The Department of Energy, Mines and Resources in Ottawa issues topographic maps. In the Yukon they're available at the Yukon Geology Office, Whitehorse; at mining recorders' offices; and in bookstores.

The National Topographic Scale is used to show distances. Scales of 1:1,000,000 (approximately one inch to 16 miles), 1:250,000 (approximately one inch to four miles) and 1:50,000 (approximately one inch to one mile) are the most popular. The principle of these scales is simple: for instance, on a 1:50,000 map, any distance on the map itself is equal to 50,000 times that distance on the ground. This can be measured in either the Imperial or the metric system.

Geological maps

Geological maps are helpful to the placer prospector because they show the type of rock in a given area. If rock types favorable to the production of a placer by detrital or chemical means are present, then there's the possibility a deposit exists.

Some of these maps are coded by color; on others the information is shown by symbols. Geological maps are produced by the Geological Survey of Canada and are available at the Yukon Geology Office.

Claim maps

Usually drawn on a scale of one inch to a half-mile, up-to-date claim sheets are kept at each mining recorder's office in the Yukon. About 700 of these are available, showing the status of all quartz and placer claims in the Yukon. At the time of this writing they can be purchased for $1.00 each.

Treasure maps

Compiled by George Gilbert, Claims Inspector, this set of two maps shows many of the proven and potential gold-bearing streams of the Yukon. They are currently available at mining recorders' offices, for $3 per set.

Other maps

Land-use maps, aeronautical maps, metallogenic (lode occurrences) maps, and old, out-of-print maps that accompanied reports made by the Geological Survey of Canada are sometimes useful to prospectors. Some of the old maps are remarkably well drawn considering that the information to compile them was put together under primitive conditions, with the surveyor on foot or horseback. Such original maps can be useful in determining exactly where major discoveries were made on the placer creeks. Other information, such as the locations of old trails and townsites and of sites where coarse gold was found, can be invaluable to today's goldseeker.

Government reports and other sources of information

Since its inception in 1842, the Geological Survey of Canada has produced hundreds of reports and maps. In the early days, government geologists usually followed prospectors and miners into an area to document their activities. More recently, this hard-working agency has actually paved the way for prospectors by exploring new regions first, producing detailed geological information and even pinpointing favorable sites for mineral deposits. (See the excerpts, under *The Bostock Report*, beginning on page 79.)

The staff of the Yukon Geology Office carries on this tradition, and the reports of their investigations are eagerly awaited by mining companies and prospectors. Sometimes a minor rush follows the release of one of these reports.

A complete set of publications is available for examination in the Yukon Geology Office library; those still in print are offered for sale. Reports by private mining companies are also kept there. In the Yukon Archives, Whitehorse, complete sets of past issues of mining magazines are on file; you can also examine old newspapers, books, reports and maps. Other sources of information are listed on page 112.

As a modern prospector, you should take advantage of this wealth of information. Winter months spent researching and studying will give you a tremendous advantage over the old-timers, who relied almost entirely on perseverance and luck while trudging the wilderness in their search for mineral wealth.

CHAPTER 5

EXPLORING THE CREEKS

You know what to look for (if you've read this far you know how to tell fool's gold from the real thing); and now you've got an idea of where to look (in theory, at least). It's time, in fact, to get down to the real business of gold prospecting.

Going where the gold is

It's time to get yourself out on the creeks and put theory to work. Although there are undoubtedly many undiscovered placers in the Yukon, it is best for beginners to go where the gold has already been found.

This doesn't mean you'll lack for adventure. Many gold creeks lie in areas rugged enough to suit most of us. It's beyond the scope of this book to address all the do's and don'ts of traveling and working in the wilderness. There are many books on the subject, some of which are listed on our recommended reading pages 124 and 125.

Experienced Yukon travelers have a great deal of respect for the wilderness, and newcomers would do well to gain experience by going along with an old hand first. Navigating, traversing white waters and contending with grizzly bears all must be part of the prospector's skills.

What are your prospects?

Short of ripping up the entire country with excavating equipment, we will never know how much gold is hidden by nature. By using all of the known theories of gold deposition; by studying maps, air photographs, and satellite pictures; and by careful research of past mining activities, it *is* possible to pick out favorable sites.

We've mentioned you should head for areas where gold has already been found, but before prospecting a site *be certain that it has not been staked by others.* (If the site is promising, you'll want to stake a claim of your own, or at least take out a prospecting lease before you embark on a test program.)

There's little real difference between thorough prospecting for placers and mining them on a small scale. Initial prospecting methods may establish that a site has all the criteria – even colors in the surface gravels – to indicate a deposit, but nothing really definite can be known until bedrock is reached. (An exception to this is bar mining, discussed later in this section).

Prospecting with gadgets

Can today's mechanical and electronic wonders help you do a better job of finding gold than the simple tools of the old-timers, the pan and shovel? You may be tempted to try them, since high claims are made for these devices – by manufacturers. I can only give you the results of my own experience with a couple of the most touted of these instruments.

A *magnetometer* or Spanish dip needle may give clues to the presence underground of certain minerals. It can locate a black sand deposit, but there is no guarantee gold will be present, despite the familiar geological association.

Similarly, *metal detectors* may turn up a nugget in a tailing pile someday, but the odds against it are high. In prospecting for gold placers, these instruments are of limited use and they're not worth the investment.

One of the more intriguing gadgets to be used for placer mining recently is the Weedeater. (Yes, the same gizmo you use on your lawn!) And, according to *The Placer Mining Times* of September 28, 1983, it's one of the most effective:

"Early this spring, two college girls began mining with their Weedeater near Steamboat Bar on the Stewart River. They began in late May and finished approximately June 10. The girls took their Weedeater to the tops of moss clumps found on the bars at low water. They took the moss upriver to some old salmon drying racks, and dried

the placer mining TIMES $1⁰⁰

Vol: 2   Issue #2

Wednesday, September 28, 1983

NEW GOLD MINING METHOD

Daryl Gallan, manager of Canamet Sales Yukon Ltd., models the newest piece of equipment used by successful placer miners, a Model 657 WEEDEATER with 4 strings and an 85 cc engine. For miners used to thinking in terms of Cats, Loaders, Sluices and Trommels, Daryl is pleased to relate the following tale:

Daryl Gallan, Weedeater Miner

Early this spring, two college girls in their early 20's began mining with their WEEDEATER near Steamboat Bar on the Stewart River. They began mining late in May, and finished approximately June 10. The girls took their WEEDEATER to the tops of moss clumps found on the bars at low water. They took the moss upriver to some old salmon drying racks, and dried it for three days. Then they burned the moss on a large steel plate, and treated the ashed through a Flying Dutchman sluice. They worked hard (but not too hard) for nearly three weeks. Their total recovery was in the range of 25 ounces of clean placer fines, from which they paid slightly over two ounces to Al Falle for the lay on his property.

Mr. Falle can show you the two ounces, and suggests that this is an environmentally safe method of mining, as well as a very profitable one. "They don't attack the roots with the WEEDEATER, just the moss itself. They do no shovelling, and create no dirty water to muddy the river. Since the moss is a natural trap for microscopic and fine gold, the method is practical, and the girls went south with a good profit. The bars will regenerate themselves, and the moss, for the coming season".

Daryl Gallan agrees that the method is practical, and suggests that he has a line of industrial-power WEEDEATERS that will produce even greater returns per day. Since the water people and the fisheries people have no reason to stop this type of mining, Daryl wonders when miners will need some special permit from the Forestry people, or the Wildplant people, or the Moss Control officers, simply to pursue the business of placer mining.

37

it for three days. Then they burned the moss on a large steel plate, and treated the ashes through a Flying Dutchman sluice. They worked hard (but not too hard) for nearly three weeks. Their total recovery was in the neighborhood of 25 ounces of clean placer fines, from which they paid slightly over two ounces to Al Falle for the lay on his property.

"Mr. Falle can show you the two ounces and suggests that this is an environmentally safe method of mining, as well as a very profitable one. They don't attack the roots with the Weedeater, just the moss itself. They do no shoveling and create no dirty water to muddy the river. Since the moss is a natural trap for microscopic and fine gold, the method is practical, and the girls went south with a good profit. The bars will regenerate themselves, and the moss, for the coming season." (Reprinted with permission.)

Geochemical prospecting can be used to pinpoint the presence of minute quantities of gold in gravels, and could help you choose a place to dig. There are also new devices that send electricity through the ground and go on to analyze the data obtained. I've never found them to be any use in placer prospecting.

In fact, it says here that the Yukon old-timer we know who religiously pans the material he finds at the rims of gopher holes probably has a better chance of hitting paydirt than the goldseeker armed with gadgets such as these.

It's going to be a long time before those tried and true prospecting tools, the pan and the shovel, are ever replaced.

But maybe there's one more exotic gimmick we should mention. . .

Dowsing

Dowsing, or "witching" for minerals, was first practiced in the Americas by the Spaniards in their search for the source of Inca gold. Although most geologists and professionals in the mining business scoff at the very idea of witching for gold, it is taken seriously by many prospectors and miners. Some won't turn a spade of earth without first having their ground dowsed, either by themselves or by a professional dowser. It's claimed that one person in ten can learn this art. While there are those who swear by the method, the discussion here is *not* intended as a recommendation.

Dowsing: wand shapes

Map dowsing

40

CHAPTER 6

PROVEN METHODS

The pages that follow trace proven methods of prospecting. You can decide for yourself what degree of effort you're willing to put into your goldseeking. You may only be interested in panning as outdoor recreation, as a means of sharing the excitement of the historic Gold Rush days. Or you may be at the other end of the spectrum, with a desire to mine for profit. Whatever your interest, you'll find out just how it's done.

Panning: the first step

Panning is a method of testing the gold content of gravels or of cleaning the gold from concentrates. It is not a mining method in itself: it's virtually impossible to obtain much gold using only a pan unless you strike an absolute bonanza. But your gold pan is your one indispensable tool. Its use must be mastered if you're serious about prospecting for placer gold, so you might as well start to get the hang of it now.

The first essential is, of course, a gold pan. These aren't hard to find in the Yukon, where retailers are happy to serve your needs. You can also order by mail, direct from suppliers. A list of these is carried at the end of this book, on page 115.

There are a number of steel pans on the market today, all of them almost exactly the same as the pans made in the old days. The most traditional are manufactured of heavy-gauge steel. If you choose a steel pan, you must take care to remove its oily protective coating – either with a solvent or by baking. You can use the coals of your campfire to do the job, or your kitchen oven. Make sure the coating is completely removed: any oil in the pan will interfere with the settling of the gold, allowing it instead to slough out.

Modern pans are frequently made of high-impact plastic – to my mind a superior material. It resists rust, acid, and corrosion, and makes a lightweight pan that's easy to handle. The best plastic pan I've found is the Garret Gravity Trap pan, with its mate the grizzly pan. This pan features molded ridges, or riffles, that trap gold more quickly and easily than ordinary pans do. For novices, this is ideal.

Here's a way to practice the art of panning without leaving home: you'll need a handful of small lead pellets, such as those you'd find in a number 6 shotgun shell; flatten them slightly. Next, obtain some gravel which contains particles ranging from microscopic size to rocks three inches in diameter. Gravel from your driveway will do, if you can't get creek gravel. Place the gravel and pellets in a pail, mix them up, and dump the mixture into your pan.

Fill a tub of water, and place the whole pan of material under the surface. Mix up the gravel and lead and throw out the larger rocks, being sure they are thoroughly washed. Now rotate the pan back and forth with a circular motion and with some up and down movement also. Shake it back and forth, left and right, then rotate again. The lead is the heaviest material in the pan and it will sink to the bottom. This effect is best achieved if the gravel is suspended in water, so keep the pan down.

When you're certain the lead has reached bottom (after at least five minutes of shaking) lift the pan out of the water. With the edge of your hand, skim off the top layer of gravel. Put the pan under water again, and rotate and shake for a minute or so. Then tilt the pan partially

Washing the rocks

Skimming the top

Shake it up

Easy washes

43

out of the water and gently wash the top layer of material over the side. Repeat the process, slowing down when only the finer material is left.

Holding the pan with one hand, wash the material with gentle flows of water, occasionally shaking the pan to ensure that the pellets stay at the bottom. Only the heaviest material should now remain in the pan, and the lead pellets should be visible. With actual gold-bearing gravel, the final result would be a teaspoon of black sand and gold.

What remains in your practice pan is lead and sand, of course, but we'll pretend it's black sand and gold. With a small amount of water in the pan, swirl the material around the bottom lip, so that it forms something like a toy train. If this is kept up, little pieces of gold (lead) will begin to form the caboose of the "train". Once you're satisfied that no more "gold" will appear, you're ready to *count colors*.

One hand now

Using the riffles

Turn the pan around

Black-sand and gold remain

44

Counting the colors

If only two or three colors (specks of gold) show up in a pan, then the stream gravels being tested would constitute *poor pay*. It could take as many as 40,000 small specks of gold to make up a single troy ounce! Six to eight colors in a pan indicate good prospects, and 30 to 60 colors to a pan indicate *paydirt* – a streambed that's worth staking a claim on immediately.

When prospectors test and find gravels poor, they often move on to try again upstream. If the colors they turn up are fairly coarse – often dropping into a steel pan with an audible "ping" – they may be encouraged enough to dig down deeper into the gravel for their samples.

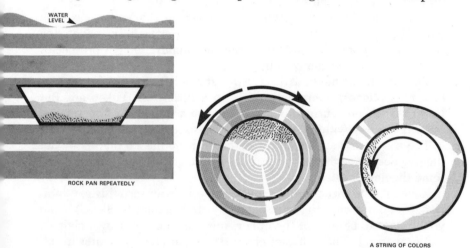

WATER LEVEL

ROCK PAN REPEATEDLY

A STRING OF COLORS

The grizzly pan

A quick panning method goes like this: drill the entire bottom of a gold pan with three-eighth-inch holes, spaced about an inch apart. This is your *grizzly* pan. Fill it with gravel and place it on top of your regular pan. Holding both pans under the water, shake and rotate until all material smaller than three-eights of an inch has dropped into the lower pan. Check for nuggets, then throw the top pan of material away. The bottom pan of gravel is now ready for processing.

Getting panning experience

You can have fun while testing your new panning skills at several commercial establishments in the Yukon, including Black Mike's Gold Mines, south of Whitehorse on the Alaska Highway. There are others at Whitehorse and Dawson. The Klondike Visitor's Association will let you pan free on its own claim – right on Bonanza Creek itself, where the Yukon story began.

Panning a creek

Once you've mastered the basic technique of using the gold pan, you're ready to put it to work on a real stream. Just follow the steps described.

Traditionally, prospectors pan in an upstream direction, hoping to find ever-increasing amounts of gold particles as they move toward to source of the colors.

More extensive methods

If your research of maps and geologists' reports indicates an area is favorable to placer deposits, yet no colors show up in panning, you may want to try some further work before giving up.

In fact, now that practically every creek in the Yukon has been panned for gold, it's unlikely that a new discovery will be made using this method alone. To evaluate a site thoroughly, today's prospector needs to go beyond the panning process.

The exploration methods described next are definitely not for novices, or for vacationers interested mainly in a little fresh Yukon air. But they're tried, proven methods that involve a minimum of capital to undertake – well within the scope of hobbyists and amateur goldseekers.

The theory is that the old-timers could have missed placers by not digging deep enough into the gravels. You're going to test this by doing some digging yourself.

Remember to check claim maps before you do any extensive exploration. You don't want to jump somebody else's claim (it's illegal) – and you'll want to be sure of the opportunity to stake your own claim if values warrant. The ABC's of claim staking are featured later in this book; become as familiar with them as you can.

Test pitting

Some wide creek valleys may have fine gold interspersed throughout their gravels, from rimrock to rimrock. This type of deposit can be evaluated by using the test-pit method, sometimes called "gophering." Gravel is thrown from the pit by hand shoveling, and the gravel is later panned for gold content.

Many test holes should be dug across the valley before a good evaluation can be obtained. If test concentrates are going to be assayed for gold content, it is important to know whether the gold can be economically recovered from the gravels. Fire assays will show every bit of gold present in concentrate, but this high percentage is usually not recoverable by simple methods.

If test pitting results in a very small per-yard value, hand mining the site is out of the question. Even earth-moving equipment might not recover enough gold to make the operation pay.

Sometimes in test pitting ground, prospectors encounter *blue clay* – a hard, almost impenetrable layer one to six feet thick. Picks bounce off blue clay, and it won't wash away. It needs to be sun dried and picked off in layers – and it drives miners to despair.

Open cutting

In a creek valley where gravels are shallow, expecially one that narrows near its head, it's sometimes possible to dig a trench across the entire width until the paystreak is outlined. The cut is made down to bedrock by hand shoveling or with machinery, starting where the old channel is thought to be. The biggest problem is keeping water out of the cut. A small dam may have to be built to divert the water around the cut with a ditch or flume. The power of moving water to cut out a new passageway is impressive: old-timers used the method to remove overburden.

If it isn't possible to divert the stream around the open cut, then a drain must be opened to allow the water to escape; if the stream slows down where it goes through the cut, it will surely dump its load of sediments and create its own dam, and more water problems than before.

In fact, drainage is a problem that must be considered in any creek valley mining operation. Sometimes drains hundreds of feet long must be installed.

Ground sluicing

Using the natural velocity of stream waters to remove overburden and to sluice gravels is called *ground sluicing*. A small dam is usually built to divert the water in the desired direction. If water is stored behind a dam, then suddenly released to increase its power to move mud and gravel, the operation is called *booming*. Ground sluicing is also used to melt permafrost.

Building a dam

On a small creek, a dam can be built very quickly by felling some trees across it, piling up debris (such as moss and branches), then using heavy-gauge plastic to block the flow of water. The pond from a dam that is placed directly across a creek will soon fill up with sediments. The water should always be only partially diverted into the holding area; any excess should be allowed to drain, usually somewhere near the bottom of the dam. Settling ponds, water storage ponds, and suction dredge ponds can all be built using small dams or by diverting water into low-lying areas.

Hydraulicking

A jet of water under high pressure is used to cut away gravel banks and to direct the gravel through a sluice box, using sweeping motions. The pressure is developed from a pump, or by using a source of water from farther upstream. The bedrock is cleaned by hand after the gravel has been stripped away. The natural flow of the stream may also be run through the box to aid in the sluicing operation.

Hydraulicking

Drilling

Sinking drill holes into the ground can be a successful way to prospect for placers. Churn drills bring up quantities of sand and gravel, which can then be panned for gold. The gold is weighed and the site's value per cubic yard is estimated on the basis of a number of holes.

Drills are often used to penetrate overburden and find the depth at which the bedrock lies.

A small churn drill

The cost of these machines, and of the expensive equipment required to transport them, limit this exploration method mostly to large companies. Even so, their drillers may encounter paydirt but be forced to leave the mining of it for the future; whereas the small operator who sinks an exploratory shaft can go ahead and immediately sluice any paydirt he finds.

Drilling is faster than test pitting of course, but results can sometimes be deceiving. If the drill strikes an underground boulder, for instance, a mistaken reading of bedrock depth can result. And if a creek valley's deposits of coarse gold are randomly scattered, the drill may miss them completely.

S haft sinking

The surest way of testing placer ground is to dig a shaft down to the bedrock. The cost incurred by two men digging prospect shafts for an entire prospecting season is low. In fact, it's negligible when compared with the cost of stripping the overburden from a claim using bulldozers, loaders, and trucks. There's another benefit too: excess environmental damage is avoided. Nevertheless, shafting and drifting (see following) are *not* methods to be attempted by novices!

Prospect shafts are usually rectangular in shape, and economical in size: 3 by 4 feet or 4 by 6 feet is typical. Many methods and materials can be used to *crib* (shore up) your shaft. (In permafrost ground, no cribbing is necessary if the digging is done in winter. But the ground needs to be thawed by fire, water, or steam.)

If a paystreak is encountered near bedrock, a *drift* (tunnel) is dug to follow it, starting from the original shaft. If an opening is made directly into a hillside it is called an *adit*. Drifts and adits are usually run on a slight incline to facilitate the drainage of water.

Many Yukon creek valleys have been extensively hand mined by the drifting method. The technique has waxed and waned in popularity over the years. Klondike old-timers had an uncanny ability to follow underground paystreaks. The price of gold in their day was $20.67 per troy ounce, which put placer gold at an average value of $12 to $17 per ounce. The only practical way to mine it was by painstaking hand labor. The following excerpt from *The Bostock Report* gives a good description of how the work was done:

Mining Methods in the Klondike (1904)

Creek claims are worked, with few exceptions, either by sinking and drifting, or by open-cut work.

The greater part of the claims are worked by the first method. A shaft is sunk to bedrock, and the pay gravels around the foot of the shaft are thawed out and hoisted to the surface. If the work is done in the winter, the material is piled up in great dumps and sluiced

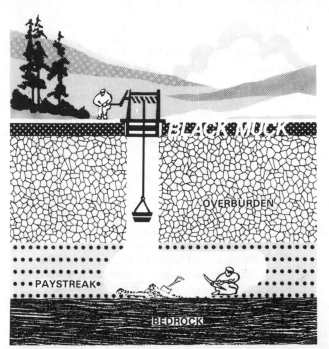

A Klondike claim

Looking up a shaft

51

in the early spring; if in the summer time, the two operations are carried on simultaneously. In the better-worked claims, a system of drifts is extended from the shaft or shafts to the edge of the claim, or of the pay, as the case may be. The drifts are connected by cross-cuts, and the farther blocks are worked first.

The gravels are everywhere frozen, and require to be thawed before they can be extracted. This was done in early days by wood fires, or by heating the water at the foot of the shafts with hot stones, but now, except in remote districts, is done altogether with steam thawers or pumps.

The relative merit of steam and water thawing is still an open question among the miners. The size of the excavation can be more easily regulated with water, as the steam, expecially in the summer time, heats the air in the chamber, and portions of the waste in the roofs thaw out and fall. Steam is used on the majority of the claims.

Timbering is seldom required, as the bed of frozen muck which overlies the gravels forms and extremely tenacious roof, and chambers of astonishing size can be excavated beneath it, in the winter time, without danger. In one case, on Dominion Creek, a muck roof, un-supported by pillars, covered a vault said to measure 140 feet by 230 feet, and remained unbroken until midsummer. Examples of muck roofs spanning vaults over 100 feet in width are common.

In working claims by the second method, that of open-cuts, the first object is to get rid of the muck covering. This is easily done in early spring by taking advantage of the spring floods and leading the water by several channels across the claim. The muck thaws easily and the streams soon cut down to the gravel, and then gradually widen their channels until they meet. In some cases, the process is hastened by blasting out the walls of the muck channel with slow explosives. When the muck covering is removed, the gravels usually thaw to bedrock in a single season. The upper portion, if barren, is removed and piled up where most convenient, and the underlying pay gravels are shoveled up or hoisted in buckets, and sluiced in the ordinary way. The open-cut method of mining leads to a more com-plete recovery of the gold, but is too expensive to be used where the barren overburden of muck and gravel exceeds 10 to 15 feet in thickness. *(Reprinted by permission)*

Open cut mining became a reality when gold's price soared to a high of $850 an ounce several years ago. Major investors sank capital into placer mining, expecting high returns. Heavy equipment was brought in to remove overburden; expensive machines sluiced the paydirt. All went well until the market for gold slid, making many such ventures too risky to continue.

Strip mining techniques, using heavy earth moving equipment, are feasible only when gold is priced very high or the ground is very rich. Generally there is just too much earth to move economically when gold prices float in their present price range although there are notable exceptions. In any case, such equipment and the burden of maintaining and operating it is out of reach of the small operator. By sinking shafts selectively, enormous costs can be avoided, and underground drift mining is a sensible technique.

It means elbow room for smaller operators – individualists who lack easy capital. Drift mining is still done by hand methods, making it a viable method for small-scale locations – especially valleys where even heavy equipment could not move the huge overburdens that cover some placers.

I checked out just such a valley myself, not long ago. The area had once been drift mined using strictly hand methods; these operations ceased in the 1930s. The valley was later excavated by hydraulicking and with earth moving equipment to such an extent that its heightened walls were in acute danger of collapse. Mining operations on the creek had therefore ceased.

But the paystreak, contained in rusty, pre-glacial gravels, was still plain to see. Its course led under a small mountain of glacial till, about 90 feet high.

There were several factors favoring an underground operation on this creek:

1. The paystreak ran uphill. This would facilitate water drainage from a drift.

2. The gravels were very hard-packed, but unfrozen. Digging could be managed without the danger of the shaft collapsing. The pneumatic equipment needed for digging in hard-packed ground is readily available, at a reasonable cost.

3. While the old-time miners had cut down a lot of trees to timber their own drifts, the bush had since grown back and wood was at hand to shore up a new shaft and drift.

There are more reasons why small drift mining operations can succeed in the Yukon. It's important to remember, for example, that when gold was worth $12 to $17 an ounce, only the richest paystreaks were worked by the old-timers. If these paystreaks fanned out and the gold became more widely dispersed throughout the gravels, then the operation was abandoned.

Individuals who do their homework have an opportunity to re-work such paystreaks, cleaning a greater volume of gravel for returns that will be higher at today's prices.

But a word of caution. The expertise you need to conduct an underground placer mining venture cannot be gleaned from books. Practical experience is absolutely essential. Perhaps you can arrange this by teaming up with someone who has experience, particularly if they've worked in hard-rock mining. With the Yukon's lode mining industry in a period of decline, it might be easier than you think to find someone to instruct you.

Try to find an opportunity to watch a drift mining operation close-up. Or maybe you can get a job in one, so you can learn firsthand how to work safely and efficiently underground.

Suction dredging

Suction dredges, which can be likened to large underwater vacuum cleaners, were developed in California to work stream bottoms that could not be mined by conventional means. Using the Venturi principle, these machines suck a combination of gravel and water through a large hose. This material is sluiced, then redeposited in the stream or pond, all in one operation. They have proved to be of limited use in the Yukon, because paystreaks very seldom follow present-day stream beds. To make matters even more difficult, the gravels of Yukon valleys, laid down during pre-glacial times, are usually hard-packed and very often frozen besides. In glaciated areas the pay gravels are overlain with large boulders.

However, there are situations where suction machines can be useful. A suction dredge is often the best means of mining loose gravels that lie below the water table. With the new triple sluice arrangements and undercurrent boxes they work quite well in bar mining and will recover fine gold.

Suction dredges do very little environmental damage compared to the old bucket-line dredges. Whenever dredging is mentioned environmentalists shudder because they immediately associate it with the behemoths of the past which tore up creek valleys and spewed tailings into huge piles along the stream banks. In contrast to this, suction dredges do not remove any of the bedrock and do not add silt or foreign material to the stream bed; what's already there is merely processed and dropped back into the water.

One way to work bench deposits is to use hydraulic jets to wash high gravels down into the creek valleys, then process them with a suction dredge. A four-inch dredge can pick up and sluice seven or eight cubic yards of gravel per hour. The eight-inch model, under ideal conditions, can process up to 30 cubic yards of gravel per hour. The jet-pump itself, fitted with hose and nozzle, is powerful enough for small-scale hydraulicking.

River bar mining is ideal for suction dredging, because the gravels are composed of small, round, loosely packed stones along with sand, and water is of course plentiful.

Dredging machines need plenty of water to work in, so dams must be built on smaller creeks to create dredging ponds. All seals and joints must be coated with sealant to prevent the machine from constantly

An eight-inch keene dredge

The intake nozzle of an eight-inch suction dredge

losing its prime. The intake pipe should be fitted with some sort of grizzly to prevent the entry of large, egg-shaped rocks which can turn inside and block the main suction hose. A full stream of water should not be allowed to pass through the sluice, or all concentrates will quickly be lost. Cleanups should be frequent.

Bar mining

Bar mining, the recovery of gold which has washed down Yukon rivers to collect in gravel bars, was the first type of gold mining carried on in the Yukon. Many early prospectors made a stake for themselves that enabled them to search for the "big one," which eventually came in 1896.

The richest gravel bars were found on the Stewart River around Steamboat Bar. On the Yukon River the best area was around Cassiar Bar, below Hootalinqua. The Teslin, Big Salmon, Nisutlin, Ross, and Liard rivers all contain river gold today. In fact, there are about 250 miles of Yukon waterways on which bar mining can be practiced.

River bars are gold-laden only in the top foot or so of gravel, usually at the upstream end. Flour gold is brought down a river during times of high water, usually at spring run-off or with heavy rains. Some of this gold has been brought into the mainstream by creeks and rivers tributary to it, and the rest is eroded from the banks of the river itself.

Practically any gravel bank in the Yukon contains gold and a large river erodes tremendous amounts of material each year. The Stewart cuts deeply through areas of glacial till, concentrating gold which may have come from faraway placers.

Flour gold will usually be found caught in sandbars and weeds, somewhere between the high and low water marks. Since these bars are replenished a bit each year, they could almost be called a renewable resource! However, a river bar that contains a gold placer one season could be washed clean during the next spring run-off and its gold deposited farther downstream.

The most successful devices for recovering bar gold have traditionally been the rocker, mechanical gold panning machines, and suction dredges. The rocker was used extensively by the early miners: there are many reports of men recovering a half-ounce of gold daily. Suction dredges with triple sluices or undercurrent boxes work well in recovering flour gold. The gravel in river bars is ideal for these machines, being composed of small, uniformly sized material.

The gold recovered from bar mining is always mixed with large quantities of black sand. Even when you recover all of the visible gold from the sand by careful panning, it will still contain gold dust too small to see. Check with a 12x magnifying glass or microscope. This extremely fine gold can be recovered by chemical methods.

56

A note on traveling Yukon rivers

Novices eager to set out in search of gold should never forget that Yukon's waterways are true wilderness rivers, without amenities or services along their banks. Many cut a course through mountainous terrain. And there are rapids, undercurrents and white water to contend with.

If you're inexperienced, *always* travel in the company of an expert. The RCMP detachment nearest your departure point must be informed of your itinerary.

Don't forget that wildlife, some of it dangerous, is always plentiful along rivers. Should you meet a grizzly bear, you'll be glad of protection, such as a short-barreled 12-gauge pump or semi-automatic shotgun, loaded with alternate rounds of heavy buckshot (SSGs) and slugs. For information on animal habits and protective measures contact the Wildlife Branch, Yukon Government, P.O. Box 2701, Whitehorse, Yukon, Y1A 2C6.

Murdoch's Gem Shop, Whitehorse

H AND WINDLASS MINE ON FRENCH HILL

CHAPTER 7

STAKING YOUR CLAIM

Getting the right to mine a promising site, or even to test it thoroughly, is not always a cut and dried situation, as it would be if you were working in virgin territory. In the old days, the procedure was straightforward: a prospector panned a stream, and did further testing if necessary, before deciding whether the ground was worth working. If this was the case, he set out claim posts in the approved manner, and hustled off to the recorder's office to register his claim.

Nowadays, such virgin territory is rare on the gold-bearing creeks. Before doing extensive prospecting, you must be certain you have the legal right to be on a site. First, check claims maps at the recorder's office for the district you're in. If anyone owns the rights to the spot you want to stake, you have several alternatives. But there are many instances where once-claimed ground may be available to you.

Re-staking old claims

The principal gold-bearing creeks in the Yukon have been staked and re-staked many times since the Gold Rush. But nobody holds such claims forever. Many do not perform the required yearly assessment work, and their claims revert to the Crown. Groups of claims are sometimes allowed to lapse by mining companies that are in financial difficulty or have decided not to develop their property. In other cases, speculators hold large claim tracts that they eventually cannot afford to keep.

It is possible to re-stake claims like these after the official date of renewal has passed. However, even if a claim has lapsed, the former owner has up to six months to show proof that he has done the assessment work during the initial year. In such a case, the claim reverts to him, even if it has been re-staked by someone else.

If you are on a creek that has been mined previously, there will be claim posts along it with number tags that correspond to the claim numbers on the placer map for that creek, and you can orient yourself by these old claim numbers. On an unmined creek, you may have to measure from its mouth or from a tributary or landmark along it.

How to stake

There is no requirement for Canadian citizenship or for a license to stake and hold placer claims in the Yukon. The Yukon Placer Mining Act governs all staking activity. Its provisions should be strictly observed, to avoid later disputes. Relevant sections are reprinted in this book, beginning on page 105.

A full copy of the Act is available free at any mining recorders' office in Yukon.

TYPICAL CLAIMS ON A CREEK

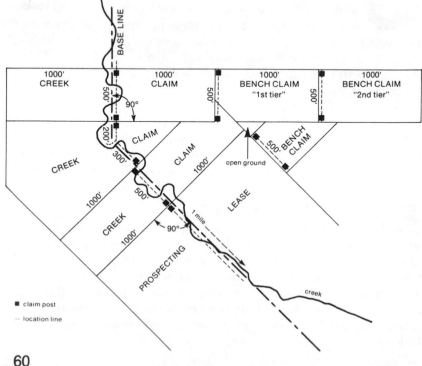

■ claim post

-- location line

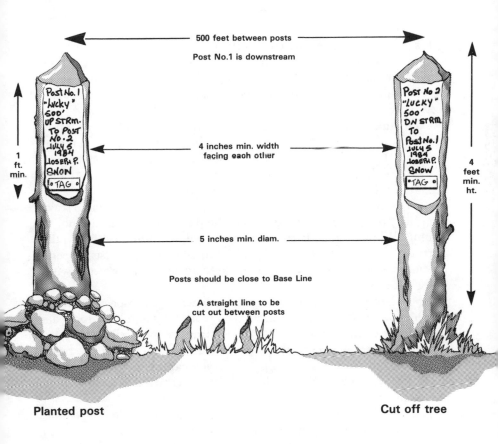

500 feet between posts

Post No.1 is downstream

Post No.1
"Lucky"
500'
UP STRM.
TO POST
NO.2
JULY 5
1984
JOSEPH P.
SNOW
° TAG °

Post No 2
"LUCKY"
500'
DN STRM.
TO
Post No.1
JULY 5
1984
JOSEPH P.
SNOW
° TAG °

1 ft. min.

4 inches min. width
facing each other

4 feet min. ht.

5 inches min. diam.

Posts should be close to Base Line

A straight line to be
cut out between posts

Planted post

Cut off tree

Buying a claim

The best claims on famous Yukon creeks have been held continuously since the Gold Rush. An outright purchase is sometimes the only way to obtain one of these claims, and the asking price is usually high.

Caution should be your byword when considering this kind of purchase. Some of the richest creeks in the Klondike are known to have barren stretches. And don't forget that the old-time miners were pretty thorough when they followed a paystreak. They may have found all the gold on a given site long ago.

It's imperative to assess whether or not the claim is worth buying, either by testing it or by seeing actual proof of test results obtained by the owner, always keeping in mind that a million dollars' worth of gold in the ground is not a viable proposition if it would cost a million dollars to recover it!

It's possible to buy claims on relatively unworked ground. There are several situations in which claim holders may be willing to sell. (Note that all transactions concerning mining claims must be recorded at the district mining recorder's office. See the sample form at the end of this section.)

Companies – and individuals – who have the equipment for large-scale mining often "stock up" on claims which they intend to hold for working at some future time. The holders of such claims may be persuaded to sell, especially if their intention to mine is affected by changing circumstances.

Rich mining territory inevitably attracts speculators, who also stake quantities of open ground – but with the purpose of re-selling, not of mining. While their activities do attract equipment and capital to the Territory, claims speculators compel legitimate mining interests to spend precious working capital to buy claims, to avoid being forced to work marginal ground.

(Speculators shouldn't be confused with genuine prospectors, many of whom are rugged individualists who work long and hard to locate new placer or hardrock deposits. In contrast to speculators, who try to turn property over quickly, propectors must often hold their claims for years, all the while trying to attract capital to develop their discovery. Most of the Yukon's hardrock mines started as the dream of a lone prospector.)

You may run across agents who try to make a living by selling claims for others. In their jargon, any claim on a creek that has been mined in the past is "proven ground." Any claim on an unmined creek is "virgin ground." In all cases, let the buyer beware!

Leasing a claim

Leasing is probably the most common (and maybe even the best) way for an individual or mining company to get into the placer mining business. Usually the owner of the ground has tested the claims and is reasonably sure of their gold content.

Sometimes a small "up front" sum of cash is required from the lessee to prove his seriousness. Then an agreement is reached in which a percentage of the gold recovered is turned over to the lessor at the end of the season or at specified times. In some cases the owner will take part in the mining operation.

A written agreement is essential. Many disputes have been fought for years in the courts because only a verbal agreement was used at the outset. Most mining contracts will cover the following points:

1. The location and tag numbers of the claims involved.
2. The duration of the agreement.
3. A percentage figure of gold to be turned over to the lessor. Because nuggets have more value than the base price of gold, a separate agreement may have to be worked out concerning the division or ownership of nuggets.
4. The minimum amount of work to be performed annually to keep the agreement in force.
5. The responsibility of the lessee to work in a miner-like manner. This means working the ground so as to not cover unmined gravels; to allow for the removal of tailings; to arrange for the building of settling ponds; and so on.
6. An option to buy the property at a set price at a later date.

Obtaining a lay

For people interested in small-scale placer mining, another way of getting property is to obtain what is called a "lay." This is an agreement by which the owner of a claim will grant the right to mine the property. The methods of mining will usually be specified, and a small percentage of the gold recovered (five to 10 percent) will be paid to the owner of the claim at the end of the season.

The advantages to the owner might include covering his assessment work for that year (using *your* labor); and getting the ground thoroughly tested or proven, at no cost to him.

Land and water use

No land-use permit is required on a mining claim or prospecting lease in the Yukon. A water license or authorization is required when waste water from mining is discharged into any natural waters, which means any river, stream, lake or other body of water, on the surface or underground. A license or authorization is also required if the dumping of tailings or overburden may have a detrimental effect on the waters mentioned above.

You can use up to 50,000 gallons of water a day, if what you use is not allowed to re-enter natural waters. The only water that might meet this condition would be the dredge tailings ponds in the Klondike. A completely closed system in which the same water is used repeatedly would also be permitted without licensing, if it is under 50,000 gallons per day.

The act respecting water use is called the Northern Inland Waters Act. A copy of licensing requirements and application forms can be obtained from the Yukon Territory Water Board (address at the back of this book). Applications for water-use permits take up to two months or longer to process. (Submissions are being made by this writer to allow recreational or small-scale mining to be carried on without the requirement of a license. The Water Board can inform you of any such changes in the regulations.)

The placer mining industry is in constant negotiation with government over regulations. New effluent (suspended solids in water) standards are being considered, but have not been passed into law as of this writing.

Assessment work on claims

Assessment work to a value of $200 must be done every year on every placer claim. Up to 10 adjoining claims may be grouped and worked as one claim with the approval of the District Mining Recorder. Allowable assessment work above the $200 can be credited up to four years ahead.

An experienced panner can process about one-half cubic yard of gravel in a 10-hour day. One man using a rocker can process up to three cubic yards a day. By hand shoveling into a sluice box, it may be possible to process 10 to 15 cubic yards of material a day, depending on the type of gravel encountered.

This gives you some idea of how the values assigned various tasks by the Mining Act (see page 111) relate to the actual work. This schedule of representation work was designed in the days of the Gold Rush; it costs much more than $200 to perform this work at today's labor and equipment costs.

Indian and Northern Affairs Affaires Indiennes et du Nord

YUKON PLACER MINING ACT

GRANT FOR PLACER MINING (FORM 3)

GRANT N⁰ P 22485

PLACER CLAIM (DESCRIPTION):
PLACER CLAIM
KLONDIKE RIVER
CREEK CLAIM
116-B-3c
POST NO. 1 is downstream. POST NO. 2 is 500' upstream.

MINERAL RESOURCES
MAR - 0 1983
DAWSON MINING DISTRICT
MINING RECORDER

MINING DISTRICT:
DAWSON

Office Date Stamp

IN CONSIDERATION OF THE PAYMENT OF $10.00 DOLLARS BEING THE FEE PRESCRIBED BY SCHEDULE "1" TO THE YUKON

PLACER MINING ACT, BY SAMUEL HOLLOWAY OF WHITEHORSE, Y.T.

ACCOMPANYING HIS/THEIR APPLICATION DATED 8 March 19 83 , FOR A MINING CLAIM, THE MINISTER OF INDIAN

AFFAIRS AND NORTHERN DEVELOPMENT HEREBY GRANTS TO THE SAID SAMUEL HOLLOWAY

FOR A TERM OF ONE YEAR(S) TO 8 March, 1984 THE EXCLUSIVE RIGHT OF ENTRY UPON THE ABOVE CLAIM.

FOR THE MINER—LIKE WORKING THEREOF AND THE CONSTRUCTION OF A RESIDENCE THEREON AND THE EXCLUSIVE RIGHT TO ALL THE PROCEEDS REALIZED THEREFROM UPON WHICH, HOWEVER, THE ROYALTY PRESCRIBED BY THE SAID ACT SHALL BE PAID.
THE GRANTEE SHALL BE ENTITLED TO THE USE OF SO MUCH OF THE WATER NATURALLY FLOWING THROUGH OR PAST HIS/THEIR CLAIM, AND NOT ALREADY LAWFULLY APPROPRIATED, AS SHALL BE NECESSARY FOR THE DUE WORKING THEREOF, AND TO DRAIN HIS/THEIR CLAIM, FREE OF CHARGE. (SUBJECT TO THE NORTHERN INLAND WATERS ACT.)
THIS GRANT DOES NOT CONVEY TO THE GRANTEE ANY RIGHT OF OWNERSHIP IN THE SOIL COVERED BY THE SAID CLAIM, AND THE SAID GRANT SHALL LAPSE AND BE FORFEITED UNLESS THE PROVISIONS OF SECTION 41 OF THE YUKON PLACER MINING ACT ARE STRICTLY COMPLIED WITH.
THE RIGHTS HEREBY GRANTED ARE THOSE LAID DOWN IN THE SAID ACT AND NO MORE, AND SUBJECT TO ALL THE PROVISIONS OF THE SAID ACT, WHETHER THEY ARE EXPRESSED HEREIN OR NOT.

GENERAL RECEIPT NO: A 04841

DATE APPLIED: 17 March, 1983

MINING RECORDER

B.J. PROUDFOOT

YUKON PLACER MINING ACT
SCHEDULE "A"
Form 1 - Application for grant for Placer Mining

(This form to be submitted in,duplicate to the Mining Recorder for the District in which the claim is situated, with a sketch of the location)

Mining District	
I,(Name)	Occupation
Of (Postal Code)	

Office Date Stamp

hereby apply, under the Yukon Placer Mining Act, for a grant of a claim for Placer Mining as defined in the said Act in

(Here describe locality) _____

INSCRIPTION ON NO. 1 POST: _____

INSCRIPTION ON NO.2 POST: _____

AND I MAKE OATH AND SAY THAT:

1. To the best of my knowledge and belief, the land is such as can be located under Section 17 of the said Act;

2. I did on the _____ day of _____ 19 ____ mark out on the ground, in accordance in every particular with the provisions of the said Act, the claim for which I make this application and in so doing, I did not encroach on any other claim or mining location previously laid out by any other person;

3. The length of the said claim, as nearly as I could measure is _____ feet, and that the description sets forth to the best of my knowledge and ability, its position.

4. I staked out the claim by planting two legal posts numbered 1 and 2 respectively.

5. I make this application in good faith to acquire the claim for the sole purpose of mining to be prosecuted by myself, or by myself and associates or by my assigns.

Sworn before me at _____

this _____ day of _____ 19 ____ } _____ Applicant

_____
Notary Public

YUKON PLACER MINING ACT
GRANT FOR PLACER MINING (FORM 3)

GRANT NO P 24223

PLACER CLAIM (DESCRIPTION)

HOT ONE   ISSUED SUBJECT TO SECTION 43 Y.P.M.A.
CREEK CLAIM ON BONANZA CREEK. FRACTION
116-B-3c
POST NO. 1 is downstream. POST NO. 2 is 218 ft. upstream.

MINING DISTRICT: DAWSON

JUL -4 1983

Office Date Stamp

IN CONSIDERATION OF THE PAYMENT OF ___$10.00___ DOLLARS BEING THE FEE PRESCRIBED BY SCHEDULE "11" TO THE YUKON PLACER MINING ACT, BY SAM HOLLOWAY OF WHITEHORSE, Y.T.

ACCOMPANYING HIS/THEIR APPLICATION DATED ___4 July___ 19 83 . FOR A MINING CLAIM, THE MINISTER OF INDIAN AFFAIRS AND NORTHERN DEVELOPMENT HEREBY GRANTS TO THE SAID ___SAM HOLLOWAY___

FOR A TERM OF ___ONE___ YEAR(S) TO ___4 July, 1984___ THE EXCLUSIVE RIGHT OF ENTRY UPON THE ABOVE CLAIM.

FOR THE MINER—LIKE WORKING THEREOF AND THE CONSTRUCTION OF A RESIDENCE THEREON AND THE EXCLUSIVE RIGHT TO ALL THE PROCEEDS REALIZED THEREFROM UPON WHICH, HOWEVER, THE ROYALTY PRESCRIBED BY THE SAID ACT SHALL BE PAID.
   THE GRANTEE SHALL BE ENTITLED TO THE USE OF SO MUCH OF THE WATER NATURALLY FLOWING THROUGH OR PAST HIS/THEIR CLAIM, AND NOT ALREADY LAWFULLY APPROPRIATED, AS SHALL BE NECESSARY FOR THE DUE WORKING THEREOF, AND TO DRAIN HIS/THEIR CLAIM, FREE OF CHARGE. (SUBJECT TO THE NORTHERN INLAND WATERS ACT.)
   THIS GRANT DOES NOT CONVEY TO THE GRANTEE ANY RIGHT OF OWNERSHIP IN THE SOIL COVERED BY THE SAID CLAIM, AND THE SAID GRANT SHALL LAPSE AND BE FORFEITED UNLESS THE PROVISIONS OF SECTION 41 OF THE YUKON PLACER MINING ACT ARE STRICTLY COMPLIED WITH.
   THE RIGHTS HEREBY GRANTED ARE THOSE LAID DOWN IN THE SAID ACT AND NO MORE, AND SUBJECT TO ALL THE PROVISIONS OF THE SAID ACT, WHETHER THEY ARE EXPRESSED HEREIN OR NOT.

GENERAL RECEIPT NO:	A 05545
DATE APPLIED:	5 July 1983

MINING RECORDER
B.J. PROUDFOOT

65

Yukon Archives

CHAPTER 8

GETTING THE GOLD OUT

So far, we're described how to find likely placer sites, and how to mine the gravels to find a paystreak. The next step is washing the gravels in order to recover the gold they contain. Panning is the most basic means of doing this, but panning can be very slow if you have a sizable volume of material to wash. Two simple devices have been developed over the years. Like the gold pan, these simple tools take advantage of the tendency of heavy gold to sink in a moving mixture of gravel and water.

The *sluice box* acts like a miniature version of the stream itself. Gravels are shoveled into it at one end, and water is then flushed through. The water carries off lighter materials (sand and stones) while the heavier metals sink and are caught by the *riffles* in the bottom of the box. These act the same way as ridges in bedrock, accumulating heavy black sand, which the miner then pans to separate out the gold.

The *rocker* is the other major hand mining tool. It substitutes a back and forth rocking motion for the forward flush of water used in the sluice box. The gravels are shaken, again in water, and the gold particles fall through a mesh to the *apron* below, where they're carried downward over a riffled surface. The gravels are left behind in the box.

Specially built sluice boxes and other recovery machines are available commercially, and it's true that such equipment does capture a higher percentage of gold from gravels. But their cost is high, too high to warrant their use by hobbyists or prospectors making preliminary explorations. Save your money until you're sure you've got ground that will likely produce enough gold to justify an expensive recovery system.

The sluice box is still the device most commonly used to recover placer gold. It is easy to build, maintain, and transport. It will wash all material thoroughly, and is easily and quickly cleaned. You can make one using simple, readily available and inexpensive materials, and it will serve you well through many seasons of gold-hunting.

Building your sluice box
The type of sluice box shown in the diagram is capable of handling from six to 10 yards of raw material in a 10-hour day, depending on the gravels being sluiced.

The riffle system
The sluice box shown has Hungarian riffles. They're among several types used in sluicing placer gravels. The purpose of riffles is to retard the progress through the sluice box of heavier materials such as black sand and gold, so that they tend to settle in the pockets between the riffles. A properly designed riffle system will create eddies along its downstream edges. This boiling effect must be strong enough to prevent packing between the riffles, yet allow fine gold to settle.

Sluice box slope
The slope (grade) at which you set your sluice box is very important. Ensure that the box is level across its width and start with about one inch of fall for every foot of sluice box, then adjust as necessary. Too little grade will cause the riffles to plug up and the fine gold will be lost. Too steep a grade is better than too little; the grade required for fine gold recovery is generally steeper than for coarse gold. If fine gold is being mined, maintain a very shallow depth of water over the riffles. This water should carry off pebbles while maintaining a loose bed between the riffles.

As you operate the sluice, watch the riffle action carefully and test the tailings with a pan occasionally to see if any gold is being lost. Most of the gold should be caught in the first few feet of riffles.

Feeding gravels through the sluice
Correct riffle action depends on the amount of material you feed into the sluice, balanced with the flow of water you maintain. The fine gold must sink beneath the material that collects behind the riffles, or it will be carried away. Stir this gravel and sediment from time to time with a screwdriver or putty knife. *Never allow water to run through the sluice if gravel is not being fed into it unless you are cleaning up.*

Sluice box & Hungarian riffles

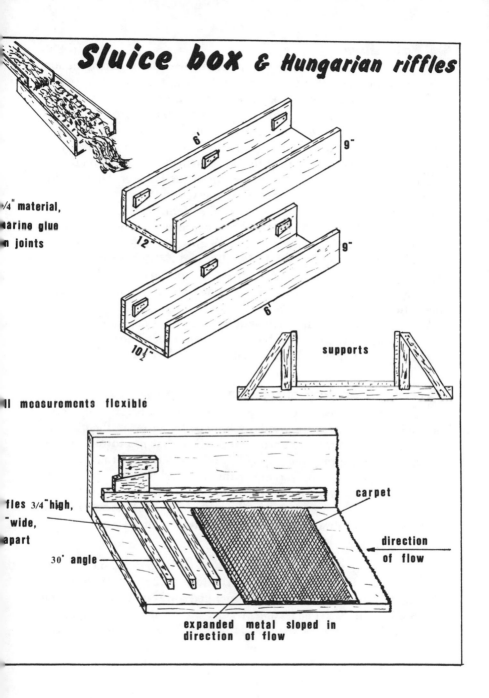

¾" material,
Marine glue
in joints

6'

9"

12'

9"

6'

10½"

supports

all measurements flexible

riffles 3/4" high,
" wide,
apart

30° angle

carpet

direction
of flow

expanded metal sloped in
direction of flow

Water flow

The quantity of water you'll need to keep the sluicing action going will vary with the size of your sluice box, the type of materials you're washing and the type of riffles you're using. For a box the size of the one described here, start by pumping about 60 or 70 gallons through per minute. A 1½-inch pump would be sufficient for this, but use a valve at the sluice box to control the flow. One way to maintain an even flow across the width of the box is to drill a 1½-inch pipe with ½-inch holes on one side, then place this at the head of the box with the holes facing downward, and feed the water through it.

It's often possible to use a gravity-feed system, instead of pumping the water into the box. This can be accomplished by digging a small ditch upstream, or by laying a small pipeline. Fire hose makes a good pipeline; it's convenient, easy to handle, and available from surplus centers and government agencies. If the stream you're working has a fairly steep grade, about 200 feet of piping would be adequate for a small sluice.

A head of three to six feet will handle most small-scale mining operations. It may be necessary to build a "pressure-box" at the upstream end to give the water an initial velocity and to keep the pipeline clear of debris.

Breaking up raw materials

Cemented gravels or clay require breaking up before they're fed into the sluice, either in a puddling box, or by allowing them to dry thoroughly, then breaking up by hand. Clay that is allowed to flow through the sluice may pick up gold and carry it on through.

By placing a screen (grizzly) over the feed end of the sluice to keep out all material larger than ½-inch in size, your operation will work faster. If you don't use a grizzly, you'll need a fork or rake to help remove stones too large to move properly with the flow of water.

Cleaning up the box

To clean up, remove the riffle ladders and expanded metal, then wash the material into a tub. The carpeting can be shaken out in the tub and washed with a hose. The suspended solids in the tub can then be run slowly through one section of sluice box using only the expanded metal for riffles. Save the processed material for a final cleanup later.

A knockdown portable sluice made of aluminum

A small test or clean-up sluice

71

Settling ponds

If you wish to mine in a really miner-like way, you should go one step beyond the sluicing process and use a settling pond to remove the suspended concentrate in the water that comes out of the sluice. A low section of ground is all you need for a holding area. You can build a small dam, using logs and heavy plastic, over which the water from the sluice will flow before it goes back into the main stream. The collected water behind the dam will give the suspended material a place to settle out. Two, or sometimes three, settling ponds are used in larger operations.

Building a rocker

The old-fashioned rocker has recovered millions of dollars' worth of gold from stream gravels. This inexpensive, proven device has largely been abandoned in favor of motorized gadgetry. However, as a machine for testing placer ground, for reducing sluice box concentrates, and for small-scale mining, it is in many ways superior to some of the expensive patented devices now in use. (I estimate that more than 36,000 gold recovery machines have been patented. This figure was arrived at after very careful research of patent records and mining journals. Very few are still in production and very few have returned their cost to purchasers.)

Rockers vary in size. A small one might measure a foot wide by three long. The large variety might be in the vicinity of two feet wide and five feet long. A rocker the size of the one in the diagram will handle from three to five cubic yards of gravel a day, at least six times the amount you can process by panning. The size shown is about average for this machine. A motorized version of the same rocker is capable of handling up to three yards of gravel per hour with an independent water supply and two men to shovel gravel into it.

Operating a rocker

A rocker is basically very easy to run. A bit of hands-on experience will quickly teach you the required skills.

Begin by securing the bed plate so the rocker remains stationary while operating. A good slope to start with would be about 1½ inches per linear foot of rocker. Fill the hopper about two-thirds full of gravel, add water, and rock.

Not much water is required because the motion of the rocker settles the gold. Two hundred feet of garden hose run upstream would likely give a sufficient supply of water on most Yukon creeks. On a slow-moving river a small pump would be required. If you're testing gravels

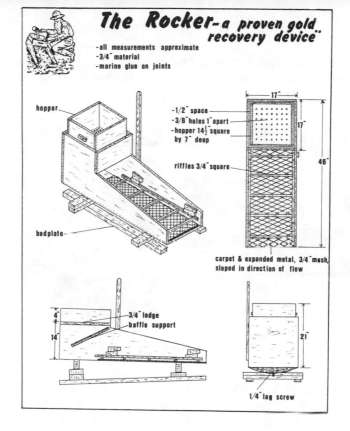

The Rocker – a proven gold recovery device"

- all measurements approximate
- 3/4" material
- marine glue on joints

hopper

-1/2" space
-3/8" holes 1" apart
-hopper 14½" square by 7" deep

riffles 3/4" square

17"

17"

46"

bedplate

carpet & expanded metal, 3/4" mesh, sloped in direction of flow

4"
14"

3/4" ledge
baffle support

21"

1/4" lag screw

A Montana rocker (built by Rick Mortimer, Whitehorse)

some distance away from your water source, fill two large containers and use a dipper to pour water through the rocker. You can recycle the same water as often as necessary.

A galvanized steel rocker

The material that collects behind the riffles will tend to pack because you'll be stopping the rocker's motion periodically to empty the hopper. This material should be frequently loosened with a putty knife, or else much of the fine gold will not penetrate, and instead will run off and be lost. Just before a clean-up, scrape up the material behind the riffles and run it through the rocker once more.

To clean up, place a small tub at the discharge end of the rocker. Lift out the riffles and expanded metal, and wash the material from them into the tub. Now rinse the rest of the concentrate into the tub and use a pan to concentrate it further.

Removing gold from concentrates

A surprising amount of gold may be left after you've processed gravel to reduce it to black sand, and recovered all the colors you can see.

Some miners throw their black sands away, believing that the amount of gold left is negligible. But an assay can turn up surprising results on some black sands which have no visible gold. They've been known to contain more gold than the miner recovered in the initial concentrating process. Many miners consider the painstaking work of removing such gold from concentrates to be a good winter pastime.

Concentrates from your Yukon placer mining operation will usually consist of gold, magnetite, and a few other non-magnetic minerals such as hematite, cassiterite, and ilmenite. Occasionally platinum is found in placer streams: it's a very heavy, silver-colored material.

To save time, screen your concentrates through successively smaller mesh screens. (Start by using half-inch mesh, then quarter-inch mesh, and finally eighth-inch mesh.) Check the discarded material for nuggets. Pan the screened material to remove all the gold you can see with the naked eye.

The material that is left should be thoroughly dried, probably in a pan over a fire. *But be careful!* There's possible danger in this process, since old-time miners used a lot of mercury in their sluices and it ended up in the creek bottoms. Some of this mercury could be clinging to your gold. *Heated mercury evaporates and its vapors are extremely deadly.* Any time placer gold is heated it should be done outside. You should position yourself upwind from the fire, to avoid smoke and vapor. On virgin ground that has never been mined before, the problem won't come up, nor will gold be mercury-contaminated if it has come from bench deposits.

When your concentrated material is dry, pour it into a paper plate. If you pass a strong magnet under the plate, the magnetite will be separated from the gold. The rest of the material can be separated from the gold by blowing it gently to one side. This method works best for small quantities of concentrates.

A faster way to process larger amounts of material uses mercury. Place the black sand in a plastic gold pan, add water till it is one-half inch above the material. Now add nitric acid until the solution begins to bubble (about one part acid to thirty parts water). *Note: doing the reverse – adding water to nitric acid – will result in spattering and possible burns.* Stir the mixture with a stick, then rinse the acid solution away in clear water. Next, obtain a wine or whisky bottle, clean it thoroughly, and fill it about one-quarter full of concentrate. Add water until it is half full then add about a teaspoon of mercury. Slowly tip the capped bottle back and forth for about 15 minutes. By now all the gold should be *amalgamated* with the mercury. Dump the concentrates back into the pan, add a little more mercury, then pan out all material except the mercury. If the amalgam will not roll into a single ball, add a bit more mercury.

Now place a wet chamois cloth over a cup to form a pocket. Pour the amalgam into this pocket. Twist the chamois tightly, forcing mercury to pass through it. Most will be separated from the gold this way, leaving a hard amalgam ball.

Heat this only enough to evaporate the remaining mercury. An odd-looking, spongy piece of gold will remain. Again, *mercury fumes are extremely poisonous.* This procedure must be carried out in the open air, and you must stay upwind.

If you want to save the mercury for future use, use a retort to recover it. Another way to save the mercury is to cut a potato in half, scoop out a small cavity, and place the amalgam in it. Put the potato back together with tin foil and wire, then bake it in a fire. The mercury will be drawn into the potato, leaving only the gold. Crush the potato and pan out the mercury.

Large quantities of black sand – 50 pounds or more – should be sent to a reputable refinery. Some gold buyers will even purchase black sands, but the price offered will be small.

Cashing in

There are four ways to sell placer gold in the Yukon:

1. The Canadian Imperial Bank of Commerce will advance up to 60 percent of the value of gold presented to them, with interest being charged on the advanced monies. This gold is shipped out for refining and when the final weight is known, the bank will pay the balance to complete the transaction. The Bank of Nova Scotia also handles gold shipments, but will not issue advances.

2. Several commercial interests are in the business of buying and selling gold. These businesses usually pay cash for gold, after deducting a fineness percentage (placer gold can be from 65% to 98% pure), refining and transportation charges, and a percentage which enables them to make a profit.

3. Nuggets suitable as jewelry gold can often be sold for much more than the market price. Some miners sell coarse gold "as is" to the many people who want simply to own some natural gold.

4. Concentrates can be sold to a refining company. Such companies usually have a minimum amount they will process and a minimum treatment charge. They may give a cash advance, sometimes up to 95 percent, on receiving assays. After refining, they may buy the gold, store it, or send it back to the owner in the form of bars or ingots, subject to refining charges.

Gold royalty

A royalty must be paid in advance, unless otherwise arranged, on all gold shipped from the Yukon Territory. It is a serious offense not to do so. Violators may be fined up to $1,000 or be sentenced to imprisonment for up to three years, or both; the gold in question may be forfeited to the Crown.

Gold must be weighed at the District Mining Recorder's Office; the royalty (currently 22.5 cents an ounce) is then paid, and the miner is issued a certificate which enables him to legally export his gold from the Yukon.

PROSPECTOR'S DIRECTORY AND INFORMATION EXCHANGE

The following pages contain factual information on the rivers and streams of the Yukon, plus details about where to get maps and information, equipment, licenses, and so on. You'll also find relevant sections of the Yukon Placer Mining Act, excerpted here by permission.

The Bostock Report

This "Bible" of the Yukon's mining industry was compiled, edited, and annotated by H. S. Bostock, from the field reports of various pioneering geologists who explored the Yukon gold districts in the early years of the century. Their meticulous descriptions of the terrain and geology of gold-bearing streams are still pored over with religious intensity by goldseekers who recognize the accuracy and depth of the information.

Titled *Yukon Territory: Selected Field Reports of the Geological Survey of Canada 1898 to 1933*, the material was issued by the Department of Mines and Technical Surveys in the 1950s. It was reprinted by popular demand in 1983, when the government was persuaded to issue a limited edition. One thousand copies sold out in no time. *The Bostock Report*, as it's known to mining people throughout the Yukon, is now permanently out of print.

I met H. S. Bostock a few years ago. He's a legendary figure, perhaps Canada's most illustrious geologist. He made many explorations, covering the Yukon on horseback on behalf of the Geological Survey of Canada. In view of the importance of his *Report*, I have obtained permission to reprint a few pages in this book. They're only a sample of what it contains; you are urged to read further, if you can. Copies of the full *Report* are kept at the Yukon Archives, the Public Library, and the Geology Division, DIAND, all in Whitehorse; and in the Dawson City Public Library.

I've selected sections that cover some major river basins and gold mining districts. The geological information is valid today; and the accounts of activity on the sites give valuable clues about the extent and type of work that has been done on them. Small-scale mining methods haven't changed very greatly in the years since the field reports were done, so readers today should have little trouble following the descriptions – especially if this book's sections about prospecting and mining methods are well understood.

The language used by the geologists is not overly technical, but the glossary at the back of the book should assist you with any unfamiliar terms.

Note that the price of pure gold was pegged at just about $20 per ounce in the years the reports were written. The speculations about relative value of creek findings by the geologists are therefore based on this economic factor. In today's world, where gold's price ranges above the $300 mark, estimates of "paying" deposits may be different. All the selections are reprinted here by permission of Supply and Services Canada.

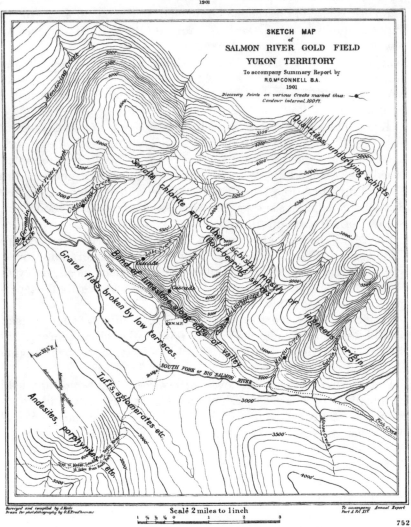

SKETCH MAP
of
SALMON RIVER GOLD FIELD
YUKON TERRITORY
To accompany Summary Report by
R.G.M^cCONNELL B.A.
1901
Discovery Points on various Creeks marked thus:
Contour interval 100 ft.

Scale 2 miles to 1 inch

Salmon River, Yukon River, and Sixtymile Districts

R. G. McConnell, 1901

The topography of the district is simple. A ridge about five miles in width where crossed by the trail, separates the Teslin River at this point from the valley of the South fork of the Salmon. The ridge is traversed by several deep depressions and is fairly regular in outline as a rule, but in places is surrounded by rocky peaks, some of which attain an elevation of 5,000 feet.

East of the Teslin ridge is the great valley of the South fork of the Salmon, a huge depression some thousands of feet in depth, and where crossed by the trail, nearly two miles in width. The valley-bottom consists of a wide, partly forested gravel plain, broken in places by low benches and terraced along the sides up to an elevation of about 500 feet. The South fork itself is a shallow stream, seldom exceeding 30 yards in width, flowing rapidly along a boulder-paved channel. It rises in a range of granite mountains to the south and has a length, measured along the valley, of about 60 miles. Its grade at the mouth of Livingstone Creek averages 45 feet to the mile.

The valley of the South fork is bordered on the east by a steep slope, about 2,000 feet in height, beyond which is a strip of plateau-like country, four to five miles in width, surmounted by low rounded hills, the summits of which have an elevation of from 2,000 feet to 2,500 feet above the valley. The plateau-strip is terminated on the east by a high mountainous district, worn into sharp peaks and bold projections, on some of which the snow lies throughout the season. The plateau-strip bordering the valley constitutes the gold field of the district. The larger creeks cut back through it into the high mountain region beyond; the smaller ones rise in the lower foreground and descend rapidly, often in a series of cascades, to the level of the valley of the South fork.

The high narrow plateau bordering the valley of the South fork on the east, in which most of the gold streams of the district have their sources and which all of them traverse, is built almost entirely of micaceous schists of various kinds, and from these rocks the gold of the district undoubtedly originated. The schists are partly of igneous and partly of clastic origin and resemble in a general way the gold-bearing schists of the Klondike district.

Gold has been found in some quantity on all the streams traversing the high plateau, previously described as occurring east of the South fork, along a stretch about 12 miles in length extending from Sylvia Creek to Mendocina Creek. The schists which underlie this portion of the plateau continue on both to the south and to the north and it is probable that the field will be extended as prospecting continues.

The most productive stream so far discovered is Livingstone Creek. This creek has a total length of 10 miles. Its general course is westerly, but four miles above its mouth it enters an old longitudinal valley which cuts off a segment of the plateau, and turns abruptly north for two miles before crossing the flats to join the South fork. It is a fair-sized stream, measuring about 15 feet in width at ordinary stages of the water, where it leaves the hills. The current is very swift, as the grade is steep, exceeding 400 feet to the mile in some places.

The valley of Livingstone Creek differs considerably in character from that of the Klondike creeks. In its upper part, it is a deep, rounded depression, evidently modified by glacial action, terminating in a steep-sided amphitheatrical basin. Farther down, the valley narrows in and becomes a canyon bounded by steep rocky walls separated at their bases by a narrow flat from 50 to 100 feet in width. The canyon portion of the valley has a length of about three-quarters of a mile and ends abruptly at the old valley previously referred to, which the creek enters after leaving the plateau.

The workings on Livingstone Creek so far (1901-Ed.) have been confined principally to the canyon portion of the valley. Discovery claim, on which the most work has been done, is situated near the head of the canyon. The gravels here and along the canyon generally are quite shallow, seldom exceeding three feet in depth, and in places the bedrock is bare. They are, unlike the Klondike gravels, only partially derived from the rock exposed along the valley, and include much foreign glacier-borne material, largely of a granitic character. Boulders are numerous and are often of large size, some of them measuring six to eight feet or more in diameter. The heavy grade of the valley renders hydraulicking practicable, and on Discovery claim the water is flumed along the bank until a head of about 50 feet is gained and it is then used to ground-sluice the light wash in the bed of the stream. The heavy boulders are removed, when necessary, with a derrick.

The gold is found principally on bedrock or in the crevices of the rock and as a rule is very coarse. A third of the gold obtained from Discovery claim consisted of nuggets over an ounce in weight, and none of it, I was informed by the manager, could be called fine gold. A few of the nuggets show a rough surface and include fragments of quartz, but as a rule they are worn quite smooth. This is probably due largely to the attrition of the sediment in the stream, as it is impossible that gold of this character could have been carried for any distance.

Below the canyon, the creek, as stated before, enters an old valley and runs for some distance at right angles to its former course. The gravel in this portion of the valley proved to be very deep. A number of shafts have been sunk, one of them to a depth of over 70 feet, without reaching bedrock. Work on most of these shafts was stopped by water before any results were obtained.

Summit Creek, two miles north of Livingstone Creek, and running parallel with it, is a much smaller stream, scarcely measuring six to eight feet in width where it leaves the hills. It heads in the plateau and, after a course of less than three miles, cascades down into a longitudinal valley, which here follows the base of the hills and runs north to Cottoneva Creek. Its valley, where it leaves the hills, is narrow and canyon-like in character, but above the cascade it gradually widens out and assumes the form of a broad, rounded and comparatively shallow depression.

Discovery claim, on this creek, is situated at the foot of the cascade. The gravels here are shallow and include, as on Livingstone Creek, numerous granitic boulders. The claim is worked by ground-sluicing, water for this purpose being easily and cheaply obtained from the cascade. The gold is similar in character to that from Livingstone Creek. The gravels deepen rapidly in ascending the valley, and work on the shafts has been stopped by water before bedrock was reached.

Lake Creek, a mile north of Summit Creek, is about equal in size to the latter and its general character is very similar. Discovery claim on this creek, is situated above a cascade, which occurs, as on Summit Creek, near the brow of the plateau. The gravels at this point, and for a few claims above, are comparatively shallow, averaging from four to eight feet in depth and can be easily worked.

Cottoneva Creek, three miles north of Lake Creek, is a much larger and longer stream and it has cut a more uniform grade down from the plateau. A canyon, half a mile in length, occurs about a mile from the point at which it leaves the hills. Above the canyon the valley is wide with gently sloping banks. The first discovery in the district was made on this creek in 1898, but the yield has been small and at the time of my visit no work was being done. The gravels are reported to be deep and difficult to work above and below the canyon, and in the canyon, where they are shallow, they do not appear to be productive. Besides the creeks briefly described above, good prospects have been obtained from Martin and Sylvia Creeks, south of Livingstone Creek, and from Little Violet and Mendocina Creeks north of Cottoneva Creek, and on the opposite side of the valley some work was being done near the mouth of St. Germain Creek, a stream heading in the range west of the South fork.

● ● ●

Thistle Creek enters the Yukon River from the east about eight miles above the mouth of White River. It is about 18 miles in length and towards the mouth from 15 to 20 feet in width. The valley is flat-bottomed in the lower stretches, the flats varying in width from 150 to 400 yards, but towards the head it narrows into a V-shaped gulch. The bordering hills have a general height above the valley of 1,000 feet to 1,500 feet, but in places slope up to sharp peaks and ridges very much higher. Terraces occur at intervals, but do not form continuous lines. The grade of the valley increases gradually towards the head. Six miles above the mouth it amounts to 50 feet to the mile, and at twelve miles to 100 feet to the mile.

The gravels on Thistle Creek resemble those on the Klondike Creeks. They consist principally of flat schistose pebbles, imbedded in coarse sand, and include occasional boulders of quartz and granite. They have a thickness in the vicinity of Discovery claim of from four to six feet and are overlaid by a layer of muck, usually from eight to 10 feet in thickness. The terrace gravels are coarser than those in the creek and have a thickness at the rim of the bench opposite Discovery claim of 25 feet.

The gold is irregular in its distribution and so far has been found principally along the left limit of the valley close to a well defined terrace. The gold is found on or in bedrock, in coarse grains and nuggets.

Henderson Creek enters the Yukon from the east about three miles below the mouth of the Stewart. It is a longer stream than Thistle Creek and carries considerably more water, but is very similar in general character. It occupies a flat-bottomed valley of the usual type, bordered by fairly steep, mostly wooded, banks which are, in places, interrupted by benches, but the banks are not conspicuously terraced.

The rocks exposed along the valley consist, as on Thistle Creek, mainly of granite-gneisses and other igneous schists. At the Forks, three miles above the mouth, inliers of white crystalline limestone associated with quartz-mica schists and quartzite were noticed, and andesites occur in a group of high rounded hills near the head of the creek.

The gold is finer than on Thistle Creek and is not concentrated near bedrock, as is the case on that creek, but extends like the Bonanza Creek gold, upwards into the gravels for several feet. It is unlikely that this claim is the only one containing pay gravel in this portion of the valley and systematic prospecting on some of the adjoining claims would probably lead to equally good results.

• • •

The gold creeks of the Sixtymile district are situated near the Alaskan boundary, about 40 miles directly west from Dawson. The rocks are similar to those occurring on the Yukon valley above Dawson. The beds have a general east and west strike, and a section across them from Fortymile River south to the Sixtymile shows two broad bands of dark quartz-mica schists, quartzites and crystalline limestones.

84

Coarse gold was discovered in the Sixtymile district in 1893, and from that time up to the discovery of the Klondike Creeks in 1896, it was one of the principal producing camps in the Yukon country.

The most important creeks are Miller and Glacier Creeks on the Sixtymile slope, and Moose Creek, a tributary of Fortymile. Moose Creek is a large stream, about 20 feet wide at its mouth, and about 15 miles in length. Its valley is about 200 yards wide in the lower reaches, but gradually contracts towards its head into a narrow gulch. Gold in small quantities is found all along the valley, but only a short stretch, barely a mile in length, commencing about 10 miles above its mouth, contained claims rich enough to work. The gravels had a depth of from two to four feet, and the gold occurred in a narrow pay streak in the center of the valley.

Glacier Creek is a tributary of Gold Creek, and joins the latter a mile above its mouth. It is a small stream, from two to three yards in width, and less than seven miles in length. The grade is steep, amounting to about 100 feet per mile in the lower part of the valley, while farther up it becomes much steeper. The valley conforms to the usual type. The upper part is a narrow gulch, but in descending, it gradually widens, and towards its mouth has a breadth of 200 yards. The valley gravels have a thickness of from six to 10 feet and are overlaid, as on the Klondike creeks, by a varying thickness of black muck.

The terrace gravels of Glacier Creek are ordinary stream wash, deposited before the valley had been sunk to its present depth, and they have no resemblance to the enigmatical quartz drift or white wash of Bonanza and Hunker Creeks.

Miller Creek, west of Glacier Creek, empties into Sixtymile River. It is somewhat shorter than Glacier Creek, about equal to it in size, and its general character is very similar. Miller Creek was considered a very rich stream in early days, and for two or three years after its discovery, it ranked as the chief producer in the Yukon country; but it is now nearly exhausted so far as the valley gravels are concerned. Terraces occur on the left limit.

Other creeks in the district are Poker and Davis, both of which head in the Yukon territory, but have their principal productive portions in Alaska; and Gold Creek, Twelvemile Creek and California Creek, tributaries of Sixtymile River from the north, all of which show prospects.

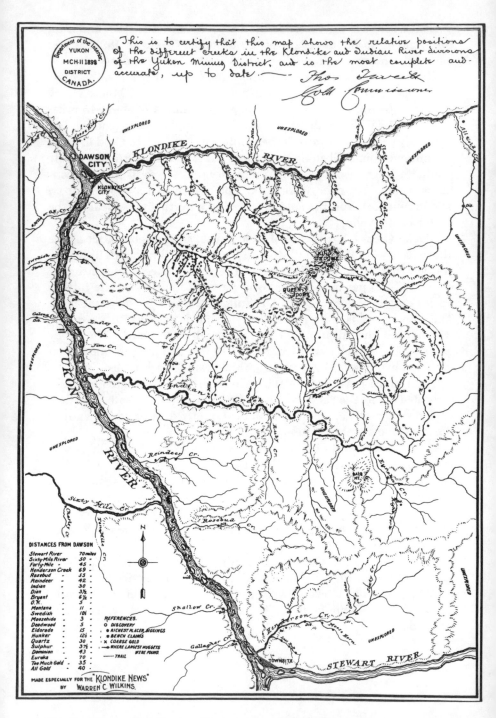

The Klondike in 1898. Reprinted by permission of the Yukon Archives

The Klondike Gold Fields

R. G. McConnell, 1903

Although the Klondike district did not become prominent until 1896, it was really discovered two years earlier. In 1894 some miners working on the bars on Indian River did some prospecting on Quartz Creek and in the following year some gold was taken out. Reports differ as to who made the first discovery on Quartz Creek, several persons claiming the honor. In the winter of 1895, Bob Henderson crossed the ridge separating Quartz from Hunker Creek and found gold on Goldbottom Creek, a tributary of the latter. He did some work on this creek in 1896, and it was while returning from a visit to him that Carmack made his famous discovery on Bonanza Creek.

The Klondike gold fields are situated east of the Yukon River in latitude 60° north. They are bounded in a general way by the Yukon River on the west, by the Klondike River on the north, by Flat Creek, a tributary of the Klondike, and Dominion Creek, a tributary of Indian River, on the east, and by Indian River on the south. The area included between these boundaries measures about 800 square miles. The streams flowing through the area described are all gold-bearing to some extent. The most productive streams are Bonanza Creek with its famous tributary Eldorado Creek, Bear Creek and Hunker Creek flowing into the Klondike, and Quartz Creek and Dominion Creek with Gold-run and Sulphur Creek, two tributaries of the latter, flowing into Indian River. Besides these, claims have been worked at a profit on Allgold Creek, a tributary of Flat Creek, and on Eureka, a tributary of Indian River from the south.

There is little doubt that the Klondike gold, or the greater part of it, at least, is detrital in origin, and has been largely derived from the auriferous quartz veins cutting the older schists and especially the igneous schists of the Klondike series. The veins are small and the number destroyed and concentrated as pebbles and boulders in the valley-bottoms is almost incalculable. The high-level white channel gravels have a volume, on Bonanza and Hunker Creeks alone, of nearly 500,000,000 cubic yards, and nearly, if not quite, half the whole deposit consists of quartz grains, pebbles and boulders derived from veins. this figure, large as it is, represents only a fraction of the vein material destroyed, as the volume of the white channel gravels was originally at least a third greater and a further allowance must be made for the large percentage of quartz ground up and carried away.

The derivation of the placer gold from quartz veins is evident from the character of the grains. The greater part of the gold occurs in irregular flattened discs and bulbs very similar, when unworn, to those in the veins. Many of the grains and most of the nuggets inclose quartz, and a few are themselves inclosed in quartz. Pebbles and boulders specked with gold are also occasionally found. A boulder from Bonanza Creek, near Discovery, weighing 60 ounces, contained 20 ounces of gold. Additional evidence of the detrital origin of the gold is afforded by its worn character in the creeks, while the younger grains and nuggets found in the gulches are always rough and angular. The richest quartz so far discovered occurs near the head of Victoria Gulch. The partially decomposed slide rock, which covers the surface of the hillside below the quartz outcroppings, contains colors of gold, and it is significant that Bonanza Creek is rich below the mouth of Victoria Gulch, and practically barren above. Victoria Gulch is itself gold-bearing, and the gold obtained from near its head is sharply angular. It is not inferred from this that all the gold in Bonanza Creek came from Victoria Gulch, as none of the heavy gold has traveled far, and the valley was probably repeatedly enriched from veins along its course, and from the older gravels, but that some of it was so derived seems certain.

The gold production of the Yukon Territory since the discovery of the Klondike gold fields in 1896 is estimated at over $96,000,000. The annual production has been as follows:

1896	$ 300,000
1897	2,500,000
1898	10,000,000
1899	16,000,000
1900	22,275,000
1901	18,000,000
1902	14,500,000
1903	12,500,000

The whole of this immense amount, with the exception of about $1,000,000 credited to the smaller camps, was obtained from the various Klondike creeks and benches and principally from the Bonanza, Eldorado, Hunker and Dominion Creeks, and the Bonanza benches. The dwindling production since 1900, in spite of the increasing use of machinery, is largely due to the gradual exhaustion of the phenomenally rich portions of Eldorado and Bonanza Creeks, and of the richer Bonanza benches, and does not mark a corresponding decline in the mining industry of the region. The number of creek claims worked, and the amount of gravel handled, has increased, if anything, in recent years, and the decrease in production must be attributed to the lower grade of the gravels mined.

The center of mining activity on the various creeks has moved steadily downward towards the wider and leaner gravel beds in the lower portions of the valleys, but none of the principal creeks, have been abandoned, nor will be for some years yet. Eldorado Creek shows the effect of seven years work in an almost continuous line of dumps, from the mouth up to Gay Gulch; many old claims are being, or will be reworked.

Bonanza Creek has been largely worked over from the head of the pay-streak at Victoria Gulch down into the fifties below Discovery. A few claims and a number of partly worked claims still remain, and it is probable that portions of the valley will be reworked. In the lower part of the valley there are still considerable stretches of low and medium grade gravels practically untouched.

The Eldorado and Bonanza benches are rapidly approaching exhaustion, so far as ordinary placer mining is concerned. Very little drifting ground is now left on the rich hills above Adams Creek. A considerable amount of work is still being done between Adams and Boulder Creeks and also on Lovett and other gulches in the lower part of the valley.

The greater part of Hunker Creek, above Goldbottom, has been worked over. Good drifting ground has recently been discovered on the Hunker benches below Hester Creek. The hill gravels are not so high-grade as on Bonanza Creek.

Dominion Creek is in about the same condition as Hunker Creek. The narrow, rich portion of the valley, above Lower Discovery, is largely exhausted, although a few claims are still working. Below Lower Discovery, the proportion of unworked ground rapidly increases. Dominion Creek, except on a few benches, has not, up to the present, proved productive between Jansen and Gold-run Creek. Numerous claims are being worked below Gold-run Creek, and the large area of gravel already proved to contain moderate pay ensures continued mining activity here for some years.

The short, rich pay-streak on Gold-run Creek has been partially mined on every claim and, in places, is completely drifted out. Sulphur Creek has not been worked so energetically as the richer creeks. Eureka, Allgold, and Quartz Creeks, all comparatively low-grade creeks, are in a similar condition.

It will be seen, from this brief survey of the condition of the camp, that, while the richer portions of the principal creeks show signs of exhaustion, there still remain considerable stretches of unworked gravel on all the producing creeks, rich enough to work under present conditions by ordinary placer methods. This industry, therefore, although it is bound to dwindle, will last for a number of years; exactly how long, it is impossible to say.

The volume of this deposit cannot be given precisely, but, from such measurements as were taken, is estimated at about 250,000,000 cubic yards on Bonanza and its tributaries. About 15,000,000 cubic yards occur on a low bench on Quartz Creek, and a smaller quantity on Bear Creek. The Allgold Creek occurrence of the deposit is extensive, but is lower grade than on the other creeks, and has not, so far, proved rich enough to drift.

While the principal values in the white channel gravels are obtained near bedrock, the deposit is auriferous throughout, and it is this fact that gives it such great importance.

The Kluane Mining District

R. G. McConnell, 1904

The Kluane mining district is situated along the northeastern slopes of the St. Elias range, in the vicinity of Kluane Lake, Yukon. It includes creeks such as Bullion Creek and Burwash Creek, draining the north-eastern slopes of this range, and also creeks such as Ruby and the Fourth of July which traverse and obtain their auriferous supplies from the bordering ranges on the north.

Indians reported the presence of gold, on streams tributary to the Alsek, early in the summer of 1903, and on July 4 of that year Discovery claim, on Fourth of July Creek, was staked by Dawson Charlie, a well-known Indian from Cariboo Crossing. Discoveries on other creeks in the vicinity quickly followed. In the same season coarse gold was found on a number of the smaller streams draining the northeastern slopes of the St. Elias range. Bullion Creek, a tributary of Slims River, was staked on September 28; members of the same party staked discoveries on Sheep Creek, near the head of Kluane Lake, in October, and on Burwash and Arch Creeks in May, 1904. The former flows into the Donjek River. All the streams draining this portion of the St. Elias range are tributary to White River. Besides the streams mentioned, discoveries have been staked on Kimberley, Telluride, Canada, Vulcan and other streams of the St. Elias range, and on McKinley, Dixie, Marshall, Gladstone and other streams draining the Ruby range. The area of coarse gold discovery extends along the base of the St. Elias range for a distance of over 75 miles, and has a maximum width of about 30 miles.

Headwaters of the White River

R. G. McConnell, 1905

Coarse gold occurs in nearly all the streams in the district except those flowing over the recent volcanic rock, but no rich concentrations have so far been found. Ruby Creek, the center of mining operations in 1904,

90

is now almost abandoned and the miners have moved on to Fourth of July Creek, a parallel stream flowing out of the same range. A few claims are being worked on Fourth of July below the mouth of Snyder Creek. A feature of the workings of this creek is that the auriferous gravels rest on a band of boulder clay which constitutes the bedrock. The boulder clay band has not been pierced, and there is a possibility that pay-gravels may exist beneath it. The gravel bed overlying the boulder clay is shallow and easily mined, but carries comparatively light values.

A large amount of work was done on Bullion Creek by the Bullion Hydraulic Co. A flume five feet by three and a half feet, with intake on Claim No. 26, has been built down the valley to Claim No. 48, a distance of about a mile. In places where the valley slopes were favorable the flume is replaced by short ditches. The grade of the creek is steep and a head of 175 feet is gained in this distance. The water is supplied to the monitor through a pipe 1,200 feet in length and 36 inches in diameter at the intake. At the time of my visit excavations for a bedrock flume were in progress. The monitor was employed for this purpose and appeared to be doing very efficient work. Preparations were not completed in time to admit of a satisfactory test of the creek before the season closed.

A number of claims were worked on Burwash Creek throughout the season, both above and below the canyon, with varying results. The values in the upper part of the creek have proved generally unsatisfactory and some of the claims have been abandoned. A stretch of fair ground several claims in length has been found in the valley about a mile above the canyon and a second one at the foot of the canyon. The returns from the best claims seldom exceed 10 dollars per day per man. Mining on Burwash Creek is attended with peculiar difficulties; the creek is subject to sudden floods and on several occasions last season wing dams and drains - the result of weeks of hard work - were destroyed by the rushing waters in a few minutes.

Some prospecting has been done on Tatamagouche Creek, a northern branch of Burwash Creek. This creek is similar in character to Burwash Creek and cuts the same rocks. It enters Burwash Creek through a long canyon, above which the valley is wide and open.

Further to the west is Arch Creek, the latest discovery in the district. This stream heads with a branch of Quill Creek and flows westward into the Donjek. Its grade averages about 300 feet to the mile. Like most of the creeks of the district the valley contracts at one point into a narrow canyon. The canyon is situated about a mile above the mouth of the valley and is about three quarters of a mile in length. Half a mile above it is a second small canyon 200 yards in length, above which the valley widens out and is bottomed with narrow flats and bordered in places with terraced slopes.

The rocks outcropping along the valley consist of hard tuffs, slates and limestones cut by several small diorite masses. The name of the creek is derived from an arch-like opening in a band of limestone crossing the canyon through which the stream has cut a passage. The slates and tuffs are traversed by small quartz veins from which the gold in the creek has probably been derived.

At the time of my visit a few claims were being worked in the canyon where the gravels are comparatively shallow. In the upper part of the valley the gravels deepen, and the few holes sunk have failed to reach bedrock. The gold obtained is found on or near bedrock, and consists mostly of heavy grains and small nuggets. The largest nugget found was obtained from No. 9 claim in the canyon and weighed over three ounces. It contained considerable quartz, and its rough surface showed that it had not traveled far. No ground yielding more than good wages has been found on the creek up to the present.

The Upper Stewart River Region

Joseph Keele, 1905

The Stewart River, one of the principal tributaries of the Yukon, drains an extensive region lying between the basin of the Pelly River to the south, and that of the Peel River to the north. It rises in the Pacific-Arctic watershed ranges and flows in a general westerly direction toward the Yukon valley.

The Stewart was one of the first rivers in the Yukon Territory to attract the attention of miners. In the year 1883 and for several years following, gold was found in paying quantities on the bars along the lower portion of the river.

An occasional miner still spends the latter portion of the season when the water is low "rocking" on some of the numerous bars between Mayo River and Lake Creek. The expert in this kind of mining is always sure of at least a grub stake.

In 1895 coarse gold was first discovered on the streams tributary to the Stewart, and from that time until the present new discoveries of placer gold of more or less importance have been made each year. The Clear Creek and the Duncan Creek mining districts were established and included all the streams tributary to the Stewart as far east as the Mayo River and its branches.

Although some of the creeks in these districts were rich in placer gold the average remuneration was small. The difficulties and expense of mining and transport, and the inexperience of many of the miners have hitherto tended to keep down the profits and to discourage prospecting.

The area, however, in which it might reasonably be expected to find placer gold is large, and, with cheaper supplies and a better knowledge of the methods of mining best suited to the conditions, future developments and an extension of the productive ground may be looked forward to.

That portion of the region which is best worthy of the attention of the miner in search of placer gold is the area situated east of Mayo Lake and south of the Beaver River.

This area is underlain principally by schists of various origin and character which are intruded in places by igneous rocks, such as granite, diorite and diabase. The bedrock of all the productive placer ground in the Yukon territory is of a similar character to the above.

Colors of gold were obtained in the gravels of many of the small streams flowing over this area, but whether there is sufficient gold to pay for mining can only be determined by the usual process of reaching bedrock.

Physical conditions on the Ladue River render it a singularly uninviting locality for the prospector. The river itself flows with a sluggish current in a wide flat-bottomed valley containing a great depth of mud, sand and fine gravel. Most of its tributary streams are small torrents heading in high mountain groups. South of the Ladue River in the area through which Rupe, Edwards and Nelson Creeks flow, conditions appear to be more favorable for mining, for although some of these streams head in high domes, they mostly flow with easy grades between low, well-rounded ridges.

In the area between Hess River and Lansing River east of the Stewart, at least four creeks flowing into those streams are known to yield coarse gold. On Congdon Creek, which comes into the Stewart from the east about six miles below Lansing, good prospects were obtained in the surface gravels.

Underground water and large boulders in the creek bottom may be expected in these areas.

Above the mouth of Mayo River the gravel bars on the Stewart, although slightly auriferous, do not yield gold in paying quantities. Beyond the mouth of the Beaver River the bars do not appear to be auriferous. The same may be said of the Beaver, and although fine gold was said to have been found in 1898 on the bars of Rackla River, its principal tributary, no colors could be obtained by the writer's party on that stream, but on a small stream nearly opposite the mouth of Rackla River coarse gold was obtained in the surface gravels.

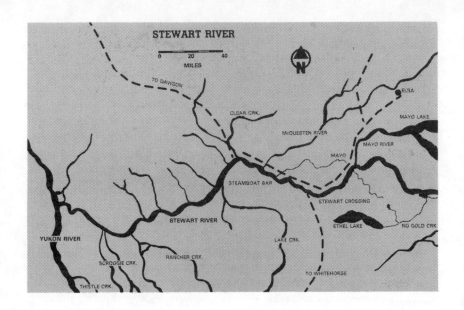

STEWART RIVER

0   20   40
MILES

N

TO DAWSON

ELSA

CLEAR CRK.

MAYO LAKE

McQUESTEN RIVER

MAYO RIVER

MAYO

STEAMBOAT BAR

STEWART CROSSING

STEWART RIVER

ETHEL LAKE

NO GOLD CRK.

YUKON RIVER

LAKE CRK.

SCROGGIE CRK.

RANCHER CRK.

TO WHITEHORSE

THISTLE CRK.

Across the Mackenzie Mountains on the Pelly, Ross, and Gravel Rivers

Joseph Keele, 1908

Prospecting for gold began on the Pelly River as early as 1882. For some years subsequently, a few miners working on the gravel bars made as much as $10 to $20 a day each, their operations being confined to the lower portion of the river. Since then prospecting has been carried on along the greater part of the river and many of its tributaries; but no mining of importance has yet been done in the region.

Fine and coarse colors of gold are found in the gravels over a large area, but no coarse gold in paying quantities has yet been located on bedrock.

There appears to be a close connection in the Yukon Territory between the crystalline schists and the placer deposits. In the valley of the Pelly, these rocks appear to occupy a belt extending for a distance of about 10 miles on each side of the river, which flows generally parallel to their strike. In the vicinity of Campbell Creek, however, the Pelly River turns northeastward, while the belt of crystalline schists continues in a southeasterly direction along the Frances and Upper Liard Rivers.

In 1875, some prospectors from the Cassiar gold fields, in search of new grounds, reached the headwaters of Frances River, and worked on some bars, obtaining gold which paid at the rate of $8 to $9 a day, and there is no doubt that the Yukon gold fields would have been entered and discovered at that time from this quarter, if the route were an easier one, and not so remote from any base of supplies.

For the last few years work in the Pelly district has been confined to the streams entering the Pelly from the south, from and including Lapie River to Hoole River.

These streams head in the Pelly Mountains, a high range, lying south of and parallel to the course of the Pelly. Along the base of these mountains lies a wide abandoned river valley, floored with wash gravels and containing several small lakes. This old valley is separated from the Pelly River by a narrow belt of low rocky hills, through which the streams have cut channels. The gravels of the old valley carry coarse and fine colors of gold, and the streams in flowing across it concentrate a portion of this gold on bedrock.

The best prospects so far have been found on some of the small tributaries of Hoole River.

The Duncan mining district, to the north of the Pelly, resembles the country in the vicinity of the latter in many respects. Coarse gold in paying quantities was found in that region about ten years ago, and almost every year since then discoveries of more or less importance have been made. In spite of the large area over which gold has been found in the Duncan country, there are serious difficulties hard to overcome, which prevent it from becoming a successful mining camp. These are: underground water, large boulders, and lack of adequate transportation to ensure a supply of provisions for miners.

Fine gold is found in the gravels all along the Pelly, from the Yukon to Campbell Creek, but none is found above this point.

Veins and stringers of quartz, which are probably due to the after-effects of igneous intrusions, are abundant in the crystalline schists. The occurrence of gold was not traced directly to the quartz seams in this locality, but the gold in deposits of economic importance has been limited to those areas in which the rocks are highly altered, and disturbed by frequent intrusions.

During the glacial period part of the ice which filled the Pelly valley came from the southeast, and moving over a large area of schists and slates, transported some of the pre-glacial accumulation of gold from these rocks. It is probable that the gold in the bars of the main river is derived from the glacial drift. The river does a certain amount of cutting into these deposits at every flood stage; the gold scattered through the drift is fine enough to be carried in the turbid water. The concentrations of gold are generally restricted to small areas at the head of each bar, and on account of their shallowness and small extent, diggings of this nature are soon exhausted.

• • •

From the superficial examination given to the country in the vicinity of the Ross and Gravel (Keele) Rivers, it appears to be a most unattractive one to the prospector or miner.

There is a marked absence of vein quartz either in the bedrock or stream gravels along the route. The intrusion of the granites in the sedimentary rocks does not appear to have been accompanied by any mineralization. The excess of silica usually accompanying granite intrusions appears to have permeated the argillites in an amorphous form, altering them to cherts. The silification of the bedded rocks is on a large scale, as there are several thousand feet of chert beds extending over a large area.

An assay was made of a specimen from the bed of quartz conglomerate which crosses the Ross River at Prevost canyon, but no trace of gold was found.

At least two parties of miners have prospected in late years on the Ross River, but without success. Chas. Wilson, who has prospected on the upper portion of the river for the last three years, informed me that he only got colors of gold in one small stream flowing into the Macmillan River, and that he found no coarse gold at all.

The explanation of Wilson's persistence in remaining in an apparently barren field is that he is in search of the legendary McHenry mine, a phenomenally rich deposit of placer gold supposed to exist in this vicinity. McHenry is said to have been a miner from the Dease Lake diggings, who penetrated to this region on a prospecting trip many years ago, and took out forty pounds in weight of coarse gold and nuggets. Various reasons were given for not returning again to his Eldorado, but he gave certain approximate directions by which it might be located, and many prospectors have been beguiled into the quest. A great deal of the country between the Macmillan and the headwaters of the Nahanni has been traversed in search of this lost mine.

Exploration in the Southwestern Yukon
D. D. Cairns, 1915

The term Nansen district as used in this report includes only the area in the vicinity of Nansen Creek. This district is about 10 miles long measured in a north and south direction, by 7½ miles wide. It includes all of Nansen and Victoria Creeks with most of their tributaries, and embraces all the streams in that locality which have been found to contain placer gold.

Nansen Creek is one of the headwater tributaries of Nisling River, and joins this stream from the north on its right bank. It flows in a general way almost due south and lies to the north of Aishihik Lake and west of Carmack on Lewes River, the mouth of Nansen Creek being about 30 miles from Carmack and about 29 miles from Aishihik village at the northern end of Aishihik Lake.

The valleys of Nansen and Victoria Creeks are wide, flat-bottomed, typically U-shaped depressions with steeply inclined walls which rise to an upland surface having a general elevation of about 5,300 feet, the mouth of Nansen Creek being about 3,700 feet above sea-level. Occasional summits rise a few hundred feet above the general upland, but throughout the district the hills are generally well rounded and have gentle slopes.

Along Nansen Creek, the valley bottom is floored with a thick deposit of boulder-clay, overlying which is a covering, in places 20 to 25 feet thick, of sands, gravels, muck, and associated deposits. The gold has been distributed through the gravels, in places being near the surface, and at other points being on or near the boulder-clay – the 'clay bedrock.'

When prospecting special attention should be devoted to the exploitation of the bedrock channels of the tributary streams, as although the amount of concentration may have been less in the small than in the larger valleys, the channels containing the gold-bearing gravels can be much more easily found along the tributary streams, than in the larger valleys; and, on the upper portions of the smaller valleys there was little or no ice during the Glacial period, and whatever gold was accumulated there in all probability still remains practically where it was originally concentrated.

Mayo Area

D. D. Cairns, 1915

The stream gravels of a number of creeks in the Mayo area have been found to carry considerable amounts of placer gold. The recent discovery of coarse gold on Johnson Creek is an example of what will yet probably happen in many other places when the creeks of the district are more thoroughly prospected, as the geological conditions are very similar throughout the district. In most places, only the present stream gravels have as yet been worked, and it seems probable that the amount of gold still contained in the deep and bench gravels is as great or greater than that in present creek deposits. The placer gold yet to be derived from this area will thus probably amount to much more – possibly many times more – than that already recovered.

Scroggie, Barker, Thistle, and Kirkman Creeks

These streams all head near one another in the divide between Stewart and Yukon Rivers, to the south of the Stewart; but in their courses they radiate out from the central area in which they have their source, and flow in northerly, westerly, and southerly directions – Scroggie and Barker to join the Stewart, and Thistle and Kirkman to Yukon River.

These creeks were all staked in 1898 and since then placer mining has been in progress on them.

These creeks all occur within the older schistose belt, the rocks exposed being dominantly schists, gneisses, and limestones of possibly Precambrian age, similar to those so extensively developed in the Klondike and other prominent placer mining camps in Yukon and Alaska. The locality lies outside the glaciated zone, which is greatly in its favor as a placer gold district, since whatever gold has been concentrated in the stream gravels remains practically undisturbed, except where it has been reconcentrated by more recent stream action; and, furthermore, the gold-bearing gravels are not overlain by vast accumulations of glacial detritus, as is the case in many glaciated localities.

98

Prominent, wide terraces or benches extend along these creeks, the bedrock of which is overlain by stream gravels which on Barker and Thistle creeks have proved to be important sources of placer gold.

The Mining Industry of the Yukon
H. S. Bostock, 1932

In Carmacks district three partnership groups of placer prospectors have been at work during the last two years on Stoddard and Seymour Creeks, tributaries of Big Creek. The two creeks drain the northeast and southwest sides, respectively, of Mount Freegold, upon which the recent lode discoveries have been made. As yet the placer workings in this vicinity have not proved profitable, though enough gold has been recovered to keep the stakers interested. As far as can be told at present the geology of the neighborhood appears favorable for placer mining possibilities. The area lies just within the limits of the unglaciated region and consequently any placers formed in the long period of erosion extending to the present, have not been disturbed. The rocks consist of a series of gneisses, schists, and quartzites similar to those of the Yukon group to which the rocks of the placer fields of the Klondike and the other important placer districts of the territory belong. These rocks have been intruded in this neighborhood by a variety of granitic rocks and a large number of mineral showings have been discovered.

In Livingstone district no new developments have been reported. There are, however, a few placer miners working on Lake and Summit Creeks and it is reported that plans are being made to re-open operations on Cottoneva Creek next summer.

Four men are reported to have been working on Iron Creek, a tributary of Sydney Creek which enters Nisutlin River on the west or right limit. They are reported to have been examining some old placer hydraulic ground near the mouth of Iron Creek, about 12 miles southwest of the south end of Quiet Lake. In the past a quantity of equipment was installed there, but no work has been done during the last ten years.

Gold-bearing streams of the Yukon

The following list includes only a portion of the Yukon rivers and creeks where gold has been found. There are hundreds more, some mentioned in the famous *Bostock Report*, several sections of which are excerpted in this book. (See page 79.)

The listed streams have shown varying degrees of richness in the past. Most can be expected to yield colors today. Whether or not you can do better than that depends on many factors, not least of these thorough homework in old records and files. Sources include RCMP files, Geological Survey of Canada reports, the Yukon Archives. *Bostock* is well worth your thorough attention. Solid, factual information of this kind will give you excellent clues about where to begin your gold-hunting.

The creeks and rivers below are identified by their geographical co-ordinates, for easy location on Yukon maps of reasonable scale. District maps contribute to ease of reference. Many prospectors seek patterns in the distribution of gold-bearing streams. When one geologist saw this list, the first of its kind ever published, he was intrigued by the fact that about 75% of the gold-bearing creeks and rivers lie on the *same longitudinal line.*

Some Gold-bearing Creeks and Rivers of the Yukon

CREEK OR RIVER	N.T.S. MAP NO. (1:250,000)	DESIGNATION (DISTRICT)	GEOGRAPHIC CO-ORDINATES 0'0"			
Adams Creek	115-O	Stewart River	63	56	139	20
Agate Creek	115-O	Stewart River	63	03	138	57
Alberta Creek	115-O	Stewart River	63	05	138	18
Alder Creek	115-A	Dezadeash	60	18	137	22
Allgold Creek	115-O	Stewart River	63	56	138	37
Anderson Creek	105-M	Mayo	63	44	135	01
Back Creek	115-I	Carmacks	62	03	137	04
Ballarat Creek	115-J	Snag	62	54	138	58
Barker Creek	115-O	Stewart River	63	11	138	54
Barlow Creek	115-P	McQuesten	63	45	137	38
Bear Creek	116-B	Dawson	64	02	139	15
Bedrock Creek	115-N	Stewart River	63	58	140	52
Beliveau Creek	105-M	Mayo	63	48	135	29
Beloud Creek	115-A	Dezadeash	60	25	137	27
Big Creek	115-I	Carmacks	62	37	137	00

CREEK OR RIVER	N.T.S. MAP NO. (1:250,000)	DESIGNATION (DISTRICT)	GEOGRAPHIC CO-ORDINATES 0'0'			
Big Gold Creek	116-C	Dawson	64	01	140	42
Bismarck Creek	115-O	Stewart River	63	37	139	00
Black Hills Creek	115-O	Stewart River	63	15	138	41
Blueberry Creek	115-O	Stewart River	63	05	139	11
Bonanza Creek	116-B	Dawson	64	03	139	25
Borden Creek	115-N	Stewart River	63	31	140	28
Boucher Creek	116-C	Dawson	64	01	140	20
Boulder Creek	115-O	Stewart River	63	58	139	21
Brewer Creek	115-O	Stewart River	63	11	139	00
Brittania Creek	115-J	Snag	62	52	138	41
Bullion Creek	115-B	Mt. St. Elias	60	58	138	36
Cabin Creek	115-I	Carmacks	62	03	137	13
California Creek	116-C	Dawson	64	01	140	21
Canadian Creek	115-J	Snag	62	49	138	43
Caribou Creek	115-O	Stewart River	63	51	138	48
Cascade Creek	105-M	Mayo	63	38	134	36
Casino Creek	115-J	Snag	62	38	138	51
Christal Creek	105-M	Mayo	63	57	135	31
Clarke Creek	115-O	Stewart River	63	04	138	37
Clear Creek	115-P	McQuesten	63	37	137	38
Cottoneva Creek	105-E	Lake Laberge	61	24	134	23
Deep Creek	115-N	Stewart River	63	29	140	52
Dolly Creek	115-I	Carmacks	62	04	137	13
Dome Creek	115-I	Carmacks	62	02	137	04
Dominion Creek	115-O	Stewart River	63	37	138	42
Dublin Gulch	106-O	Nash Creek	64	03	135	48
Duncan Creek	105-M	Mayo	63	46	135	31
Edmonton (Battleford)	105-M	Mayo	63	47	134	49
Eldorado Creek	115-O	Stewart River	63	55	139	19
Eliza Creek	115-I	Carmacks	62	05	137	11
Eureka Creek	115-O	Stewart River	63	38	138	49
Ferguson Creek	115-A	Dezadeash	60	40	137	55
Finlayson River	105-H	Frances Lake	61	29	129	42
Firth River	117-D	Herschel Island	69	33	139	32
Fivemile Creek	116-C	Dawson	64	02	140	39
Flat Creek	115-O	Stewart River	63	57	138	37
Fortymile River	116-C	Dawson	64	26	140	32
Fourth of July Creek	115-G	Kluane Lake	61	07	138	02

CREEK OR RIVER	N.T.S. MAP NO. (1:250,000)	DESIGNATION (DISTRICT)	GEOGRAPHIC CO-ORDINATES 0'0'			
Glacier Creek	116-C	Dawson	64	01	140	43
Gold Bottom Creek	115-0	Stewart River	63	58	138	58
Gold Run Creek	115-0	Stewart River	63	41	138	35
Goring Creek	116-B	Dawson	64	03	138	53
Haggart Creek	115-P	McQuesten	63	54	136	01
Hamilton Creek	116-A	Larsen Creek	64	04	137	30
Hayes Creek	115-J	Snag	62	43	114	00
Henderson Creek	115-0	Stewart River	63	21	139	27
Hester Creek	115-0	Stewart River	63	59	139	02
Highet Creek	115-P	McQuesten	63	43	136	04
Hunker Creek	116-B	Dawson	64	02	139	13
Indian River	115-0	Stewart River	63	47	139	44
Iron Creek	115-0	Stewart River	63	05	138	56
Jarvis River	115-B	Mt. St. Elias	60	46	138	09
Johnson Creek	115-P	McQuesten	63	49	136	27
Keystone Creek	105-M	Mayo	63	47	135	12
Kirkman Creek	115-J	Snag	62	59	139	23
Klondike River	116-B	Dawson	64	03	139	26
Koidern River	115-F	Kluane Lake	62	03	140	27
Lake Creek	105-E	Lake Laberge	61	22	134	23
Lapie River	105-K	Tay River	62	02	132	36
Last Chance Creek	116-B	Dawson	64	01	139	06
Lepine Creek	116-B	Dawson	64	05	139	05
Liard River	105-A	Watson Lake	60	00	128	35
Lightning Creek	105-M	Mayo	63	54	135	21
Lindow Creek	115-0	Stewart River	63	59	139	13
Little Bear Creek	105-E	Lake Laberge	61	03	134	04
Little Blanche Creek	115-0	Stewart River	63	49	139	04
Little Violet Creek	105-E	Lake Laberge	61	25	134	24
Livingstone Creek	105-E	Lake Laberge	61	22	134	23
Lynx Creek	105-M	Mayo	63	59	135	51

CREEK OR RIVER	N.T.S. MAP NO. (1:250,000)	DESIGNATION (DISTRICT)	GEOGRAPHIC CO-ORDINATES 0'0			
Machete Creek	105-E	Lake Laberge	61	03	134	00
Maisy Mae Creek	115-O	Stewart River	63	14	138	49
Mariposa Creek	115-J	Snag	62	59	138	34
Matson Creek	115-N	Stewart River	63	43	140	12
McIntyre Creek	115-P	McQuesten	63	43	136	07
McLagon Creek	115-P	McQuesten	63	41	136	11
McQuesten River	115-P	McQuesten	63	33	137	27
Miller Creek	115-N	Stewart River	63	59	140	48
Minto Creek	105-M	Mayo	63	42	135	52
Montana Creek	115-O	Stewart River	63	42	138	58
Moose Creek	105-E	Lake Laberge	61	17	134	18
Moose Creek	116-C	Dawson	64	17	141	00
Nansen Creek	115-I	Carmacks	62	02	137	13
Newbauer Creek	115-I	Carmacks	62	02	137	12
Nisutlin River	115-J	Snag	62	29	139	29
No Name Creek	116-B	Dawson	64	09	139	29
Pan Creek	115-F	Kluane Lake	62	00	140	53
Parent Creek	105-M	Mayo	63	50	135	27
Pelly River	115-J	Carmacks	62	47	137	20
Poker Creek	116-C	Dawson	64	03	141	00
Portland Creek	115-O	Stewart River	63	49	138	40
Preacher Creek	115-O	Stewart River	63	10	138	53
Primrose Creek	115-A	Dezadeash	60	28	136	06
Rice Creek	115-N	Stewart River	63	15	140	51
Roaring Fork Creek	105-M	Mayo	63	43	136	00
Rosebud Creek	115-O	Stewart River	63	17	138	26
Rusk Creek	115-I	Carmacks	62	04	137	14
Sayyea Creek	105-B	Wolf Lake	60	45	130	25
Scroggie Creek	115-O	Stewart River	63	12	138	51
Scurvy Creek	105-B	Wolf Lake	60	49	130	33
Selwyn River	115-J	Snag	62	48	138	17
Seymour Creek	115-I	Carmacks	62	21	137	11
Sheep Creek	117-C	Demarcation Point	69	09	140	09
Shootanook Creek	105-B	Wolf Lake	60	49	131	00
Shorty Creek	115-A	Dezadeash	60	24	137	10

CREEK OR RIVER	N.T.S. MAP NO. (1:250,000)	DESIGNATION (DISTRICT)	GEOGRAPHIC CO-ORDINATES 0'0"			
Sidney Creek	105-C	Teslin	60	46	132	57
Silver Creek	115-A	Dezadeash	60	02	137	11
Sixtymile River	115-0	Stewart River	63	34	139	46
Slate Creek	115-I	Carmacks	62	05	137	13
Squaw Creek	115-P	McQuesten	63	47	137	28
Steele River	115-0	Stewart River	63	37	139	01
Steep Creek	105-M	Mayo	63	42	134	57
Stewart River	115-0	Stewart River	63	19	139	24
Stoddart Creek	115-I	Carmacks	62	22	137	08
Sulphur Creek	115-0	Stewart River	63	45	138	53
Summit Creek	105-E	Lake Laberge	61	23	134	22
Swede Creek	116-B	Dawson	64	01	139	34
Tagish Creek	105-D	Whitehorse	60	19	134	16
Tatamagouche Creek	115-G	Kluane Lake	61	22	139	19
Tenmile Creek	115-0	Stewart River	63	33	139	55
Teraktu Creek	105-E	Lake Laberge	61	39	134	30
Teslin River	105-E	Lake Laberge	61	34	134	54
Thistle Creek	115-0	Stewart River	63	04	139	29
Twelfth of July Creek	115-G	Kluane Lake	61	10	138	04
Twelvemile Creek	115-0	Stewart River	63	13	139	51
Wallhalla Creek	115-0	Stewart River	63	07	138	37
Webber Creek	115-I	Carmacks	62	03	137	13
Williams Creek	105-M	Mayo	63	50	135	28
Zinc Creek	115-P	McQuesten	63	47	137	40

Mining districts and offices

The Yukon has been divided into four mining districts, each presided over by a mining recorder. You'll be welcomed as a visitor to any of the offices listed, but it's suggested that you do not ask them to mail you information. Personal visits are well worthwhile. You can check on the claim status of every gold-bearing creek in a district, or buy up-to-date claim maps. You can also view and purchase claim sheets at the supervising recorder's office in Whitehorse; note that information is not kept so up-to-date as it is in the district offices. A map is found in the back of this book, on page 132.

Mining Recorder
Dawson Mining District
Box 249
Dawson City, Yukon Y0E 1G0

Mining Recorder
Mayo Mining District
Box 10
Mayo, Yukon Y0B 1M0

Mining Recorder
Whitehorse Mining District
Room 220
Federal Building
Whitehorse, Yukon Y1A 2B5

Mining Recorder
Watson Lake Mining District
Box 269
Watson Lake, Yukon Y0A 1C0

Supervising Mining
Recorder's Office
Department of Indian and
Northern Affairs Canada
200 Range Road
Whitehorse, Yukon Y1A 3V1

Excerpts from the Yukon Placer Mining Act

Chapter Y-3
An Act respecting placer mining in the
Yukon Territory.

Short Title
1. This Act may be cited as the
Yukon Placer Mining Act
R.S.,c. 300,s.l.

Interpretation
Definitions
2. (1) in this Act

"base line" (ligne)
"base line" of a creek or river
means a traverse line following
the general direction of the center
bottom lands of the valley of the
creek or river, surveyed and
established under the direction
and with the approval of the
Commissioner;

"claim" "mining property" (claim)
"claim" means any parcel of land
located or granted for placer
mining, and "mining property"
includes besides claims, any
ditches or water rights used for
mining thereon, and all other
things belonging thereto or used

in the working thereof for mining
purposes;

"Commissioner", etc. (commissaire)
"Commissioner," "Council" and
"Commissioner in Council," respectively, have the same meaning
as they have in the Yukon Act;

"creek" (creek)
"creek" means all natural water-
courses, whether usually containing water or not; and that portion
of any stream below the point
where it enters the valley of the
parent stream; but does not include streams that may be considered rivers under the dredging
regulations, that is, streams
having an average width of one
hundred and fifty feet;

"legal post" (borne)
"legal post" means a stake having
a diameter throughout of not less
than five inches, standing not less
than four feet above the ground
and flatted on two sides for at
least one foot from the top, each

of the sides so flatted measuring at least four inches across the face, and includes also any stump or tree cut off and flatted or faced to the aforesaid height and size.

Right to Acquire Claims

Who may locate claims

17. (1) Subject to this Act, any individual eighteen years of age or over, on his own behalf, on behalf of any corporation authorized to carry on business in the Territory, or on behalf of any other individual eighteen years of age or over, may enter for mining purposes, locate, prospect and mine for gold and other precious minerals or stones upon any lands in the Territory.

Restrictions on locating claims

(2) Subsection (1) does not apply to lands

(a) to which the National Parks Act applies;

(b) used as a cemetery or burial ground;

(c) lawfully occupied for placer mining purposes;

(d) set apart and appropriated by the Governor in Council for any purpose described in paragraph 19(d) of the Territorial Lands Act;

(e) entry on which the purpose of prospecting for minerals and locating a claim is prohibited by order of the Governor in Council under section 93 of this Act except on the terms and conditions set out in the order;

(f) under the administration and control of the Minister of National Defence, unless the consent of that Minister has been obtained in writing;

(g) withing the boundaries of a city, town or village as defined by any ordinance of the Commissioner in Council, unless under regulations approved by the Governor in Council; or

(h) occupied by a building or within the curtilage of a dwelling house. R.S.,c. 49 (1st Supp.),s.l.

Security for damages

18. No person shall enter for mining purposes, locate, prospect or mine upon lands owned or lawfully occupied by another until he has given adequate security, to the satisfaction of the mining recorder, for any loss or damage that may be thereby caused, and persons so entering, locating, prospecting or mining upon any such lands shall make full compensation to the owner or occupant of such lands for any loss or damage so caused, such compensation, in case of dispute, to be determined by a court having jurisdiction in mining disputes. R.S.,c. 300,s. 18

Size, Form, etc, of Claims

Nature and size of claims

20. (1) A claim on a creek shall not exceed five hundred feet in length, measured along the base line of the creek, established or to be established by a Government survey, as hereinafter provided.

Side boundaries

(2) The side boundaries of a claim shall be lines on either side of the base line, parallel thereto and one thousand feet distant therefrom.

End boundaries

(3) The end boundaries of the claim shall be lines drawn at each end of the claim, at right angles to the baseline, and extending not more than one thousand feet on either side thereof.

If base line not established

(4) In the event of the base line not being established, the claim may be staked along the general direction of the valley of the creek, but in such case, when the base line is established, the boundaries thereby defined shall be conformed to R.S.,c. 300, s. 20.

Claims elsewhere than on a creek

21. A claim situated elsewhere than on a creek shall not exceed five hundred feet in length parallel to the base line of the creek toward which it fronts, by one thousand feet. R.S.,c. 300, s. 21.

Claims fronting on a creek

22. A claim fronting on a creek or river shall be staked as nearly as possible parallel to the general direction of the valley of the creek or river, and shall conform to the boundaries that the base line, when established, defines. R.S.,c. 300, s. 22.

How measured

23. Claims shall be measured horizontally irrespective of inequalities on the surface of the ground. R.S.,c. 300, s. 23.

Form of claims

24. (1) Every creek claim shall be as nearly as possible rectangular in form, and shall be marked by two legal posts firmly fixed in the ground on the base line at each end of the claim.

Idem

(2) A claim situated elsewhere than on a creek shall be as nearly as possible rectangular in form, and shall be marked by two legal posts firmly fixed in the ground in a line parallel to the base line and on the side nearest the creek or river toward which it fronts.

Line between posts

(3) The line between the two posts shall be well cut out so that one post may, if the nature of the surface will permit, be seen from the other.

Marking posts

(4) One of the flatted sides of each post shall face the claim, and on each post shall be written on the side facing the claim, a legible notice stating the name or number of the claim, or both if possible, its length in feet, the date when staked, and the full Christian and surname of the locator.

Numbering of posts

(5) The posts shall be numbered 1 and 2 respectively, and it is not lawful to move them except that No. 2 may be moved by a Dominion land surveyor, if the distance between the posts exceeds the length prescribed by this Act, but not otherwise.

Saving

(6) Notwithstanding anything herein contained, failure on the part of a locator of a claim to comply with any of the foregoing provisions of this section shall not be deemed to invalidate his location, if, upon the facts, it appears to the satisfaction of the mining recorder that there has been on the part of the locator a bone fide attempt to comply with this Act, and that the non-observance of the formalities hereinbefore referred to is not of a character calculated to mislead other persons desiring to locate claims in the vicinity. R.S.,c. 300, s. 24.

Size of discovery claims

25. Any person or party of persons locating the first claim on any creek, hill, bench, bar or plain or locating a claim on any creek, hill, bench, bar or plain upon which there is no recorded claim, is entitled to a claim or claims respectively of the following size, namely,

(a) one locator, one claim, fifteen hundred feet in length; and

(b) a party of two or more locators, two claims, each one thousand two hundred and fifty feet in length; and for each member of the party beyond two a claim of the ordinary size only. R.S.,c. 300, s. 25.

Locating and Recording

Forms

27. The forms of application for grant, of application for renewal of grant, and of grant of a claim are those contained respectively in Forms, 1, 2 and 3 of Schedule 1. R.S.,c. 300, s. 27.

Time allowed

28. (1) An application in duplicate for a grant of a claim shall be filed with the mining recorder within ten days after the location thereof, if it is located within ten miles of the mining recorder's office.

Extra time

(2) One extra day shall be allowed for every additional ten miles or fraction thereof. R.S.,c. 300, s. 28.

Disputes

Title

75. In the case of any dispute as to the locating of a claim, the title to the claim shall depend upon priority of location, subject, however to any question as to the validity of the record itself, and subject further to the claimant having complied with all the terms and conditions of the Act. R.S.,c. 300, s. 75.

General

Misrepresentation, removal of legal posts, etc.

89. (1) If it is proved to the satisfaction of the mining recorder that any person has

(a) been guilty of misrepresentation in the statement sworn to by him in recording any claim, or in any of the statements required, under this Act, to be made by him under oath, or

(b) removed, or disturbed with intent to remove, or defaced any legal post or stake or other mark placed under the provisions of this Act, the mining recorder may, in his discretion, order that such person be debarred from the right to obtain a grant or renewal of a grant of a claim for any length of time that he deems advisable.

Notification

(2) The mining recorder shall, forthwith, upon any such decision by him, notify every other mining recorder of such decision.

Appeal

(3) An appeal lies from any such decision of the mining recorder to the Commissioner. R.S.,c. 300, s. 89.

Lease to Prospect

92. (1) The Commissioner may grant a lease to prospect for the purposes of placer mining as defined in the Act on lands that are the property of the Crown, or the mining rights of which are

available for disposal under this Act, upon receipt of an application accompanied by evidence to his satisfaction of the applicant's financial ability and intention to incur the expenditure necessary to thoroughly prospect the area described in the application.

Location

(2) The location shall be marked in the ground in the manner prescribed by this Act, and application for a lease shall be submitted in the form prescribed in Form 6 of Schedule 1.

No other application

(3) While the lease remains in force the lessee is not eligible to make application for another lease.

Term of lease

(4) The term of the lease shall be one year, renewable for two additional periods of one year each, if the lessee on or before the termination of the year furnishes the Commissioner with evidence to show that he has incurred the prescribed expenditure in prospecting operations, and has otherwise complied with this Act and with the terms and conditions of the lease.

Application for lease of abandoned ground

(5) If the tract included in an application for a lease comprises abandoned ground, that is, if the whole or any portion of the creek or river upon which the tract applied for is situated has previously been staked out and recorded under this Act, or the regulations that preceded it, or under the hydraulic mining regulations approved by Order in Council dated the 3rd day of December 1898, but the grants of which have been permitted to lapse, or have been cancelled or forfeited, it shall not exceed five miles in length, and in the case of a creek shall be measured along the base line in the manner prescribed in this Act, the side and end boundaries of the location being those defined in this Act.

Location on river

(6) In the case of a river, the location shall be on one side thereof only, and shall extend back from the foot of the natural banks a distance of one thousand feet measured from the base line, the end boundaries being lines drawn at each end of the location at right angles to such base line.

Size of locations

(7) Locations other than on a creek or river shall not exceed one thousand feet in width and five miles in length measured along the line parallel to the base line of the creek or river and shall be made only on abandoned ground as defined in subsection (5).

Rental

(8) The rental of the tract leased shall be at the rate of twenty-five dollars a mile or fraction of a mile, payable to the Commissioner in advance for each year.

Evidence of expenditure

(9) Prior to the termination of the year the lessee shall furnish evidence, supported by affidavit, to the satisfaction of the Commissioner, that he has incurred during the year an expenditure at the rate of at least one thousand dollars for each mile or fraction

of a mile leased to him in prospecting operations by recognized methods on the location itself, or for any purpose that to the Commissioner may seem essential or necessary for the economical development of the tract leased; and if such evidence is not furnished before the termination of the year, or is not satisfactory, the lessee is not entitled to a renewal of his lease.

Lessee may stake out claims

(10) Before the termination of the lease the lessee may, if he so desires, personally stake out in the manner prescribed in this Act, placer mining claims comprising the whole or any portion of the tract leased, and upon furnishing the Commissioner with satisfactory evidence to show that he has incurred during the year for which the lease was issued the expenditure already provided for in the development of the leasehold he may submit application in the form prescribed in Form 1 of Schedule 1, and obtain a grant in his own name for each of the claims so staked and applied for, in which case the unrecorded portion of the location immediately reverts to the Crown and becomes available for disposal under this Act.

Lease upon creek or river not already prospected

(11) If a creek or a river upon which an applicant desires to acquire a lease to prospect has not already been prospected, that is, if mining claims have not previously been staked, recorded, and abandoned along any part of such creek or river, the term of the lease that may be granted shall be for one year only, not subject to renewal and the tract leased shall not exceed one mile in length, marked out and measured in the manner above prescribed, and subject to all the conditions above set out in so far as they can be made to apply.

Evidence of expenditure

(12) Before the termination of the year the lessee of such location may, if he so desires, stake out within the limits of the tract leased a claim not exceeding in size a discovery claim as defined in this Act, and upon furnishing the Commissioner with satisfactory evidence to show that he has incurred during the year for which the lease was issued the expenditure already provided for in the development of the leasehold, he may submit application and obtain a grant for the claim so staked and applied for, in which case the unrecorded portion of the location immediately reverts to the Crown and becomes available under this Act, and only one discovery claim shall be allowed on any such creek or river.

Fees

(13) The fee for the issue of a lease, or for the renewal thereof, is twenty-five dollars for each mile or fraction of a mile described in the lease, payable in advance to the mining recorder for the district, or to the Commissioner.

Transfers

(14) The lessee shall not assign, transfer or sublet the rights described in the lease, or any portion thereof, without the consent in writing of the Minister being first had and obtained. R.S.,c. 300, s. 92.

Allowable Work and Costs

Shaft sinking

For first 10 feet in depth	$3.00	per running foot of dirt removed
For second 10 feet in depth	$6.00	per running foot of dirt removed
For third 10 feet in depth	$9.00	per running foot of dirt removed
For fourth 10 feet in depth	$12.00	per running foot of dirt removed
Below 40 feet in depth	$15.00	per running foot of dirt removed

Tunneling

(a) In unfrozen ground, for first 25 feet, $3.00 per running foot; beyond 25 feet, $4.50 per running foot.

(b) In frozen ground, for first 25 feet, $4.50 per running foot; beyond 25 feet, $6.00 per running foot.

Drifting from shaft

(a) In unfrozen ground, $3.00 per running foot.

(b) In frozen ground, $4.50 per running foot.

There shall be allowed, in addition, $1.50 per running foot for every 10 feet in depth of the shaft from which the drift is run. In the measuring of the drift, each running foot shall have a width of four feet, and where the drift is of a greater width, allowance shall be made for such additional work on a basis of each running foot having a width of four feet.

Timbering

In shaft, $4.50 per running foot.
In drift or tunnel, $8.00 per running foot.

Open cutting

(a) Ground sluicing, 75¢ per cubic yard of dirt removed.

(b) Stripping (by scraper), $1.12 per cubic yard of dirt removed.

(c) Hand-shoveling, $2.62 per cubic yard of dirt removed.

Drilling

In all cases, including both power and hand drilling, the actual cost of such work.

Hydraulicking, dredging and power shoveling

$1.00 per cubic yard.

Wood

The cutting and hauling of wood outside the limits of a placer claim shall not be allowed as representation work, as such cost is already provided for in the various classifications of work set out above.

Unprovided cases

Other minerlike work for which special provision is not made shall be allowed at the actual cost, but for ordinary labor $15.00 per day per man employed shall be allowed.

All mining operations for the purpose of representing claims shall be done in a minerlike manner. *(Reprinted by permission of Supply and Services Canada)*

Getting the information you want: where to write

For specific information on the following:

Topographical, aeronautical, geological maps
Canada Map Office
Energy, Mines and Resources
Canada
580 Booth St.
Ottawa, Ontario K1A 0E4

Canada Map Office
Geology Branch
Indian and Northern Affairs
Canada
200 Range Road
Whitehorse, Yukon Y1A 3V1

Road maps
Tourism Yukon
Department of Economic
Development and Tourism
Administration Building
Second Avenue & Hanson Street
P.O. Box 2703
Whitehorse, Yukon Y1A 2C6

Publications
Canadian Government
Publishing Centre
Supply and Services Canada
Ottawa, Ontario K1A 0S9

Geology
Regional Geologist
Geology Division
Indian and Northern Affairs
Canada
200 Range Road
Whitehorse, Yukon Y1A 3V1

Game Management
Chief, Wildlife Management
Department of Renewable
Resources
Government of Yukon
10 Burns Road
P.O. Box 2703
Whitehorse, Yukon Y1A 2C6

Land Use
Head, Land Use
Northern Affairs Program
200 Range Road
Whitehorse, Yukon Y1A 3V1

Customs & Excise
Area Collector of Customs
CP 4520
Whitehorse, Yukon Y1A 2R8

Immigration
Employment and Immigration
Canada
Room 101, Federal Building
308 Main Street
Whitehorse, Yukon Y1A 2B5

Water Rights
Yukon Territory Water Board
Suite 200
4114 Fourth Avenue
Whitehorse, Yukon Y1A 4N7

Blasting Permits
Regional Mining Engineer
Northern Affairs Program
Indian and Northern Affairs
Canada
200 Range Road
Whitehorse, Yukon Y1A 3V1

Environment
District Director
Environmental Protection
Service
Environment Canada
Federal Building
Room 225
308 Main Street
Whitehorse, Yukon Y1A 2B5

Fish
District Supervisor
Fisheries and Oceans Canada
112 Industrial Road
Whitehorse, Yukon Y1A 2T9

Mineral Rights
Regional Manager of Mineral
Rights
Northern Affairs Program
Indian and Northern Affairs
Canada
200 Range Road
Whitehorse, Yukon Y1A 3V1

Aerial photographs

National Air Photo Library
Energy, Mines and Resources
Canada
615 Booth St.
Ottawa, Ontario K1A 0E9

Regional Surveyor, Legal
Surveys Division
Surveys and Mapping Branch
Energy, Mines and Resources
Canada
Room 208
204 Range Road
Whitehorse, Yukon Y1A 3V1

114

Canadian Treasure Trail
P.O. Box 2210D
Camden East, Ontario K0K 100
(metal detectors, dredges)

Diversified Electronics of
Canada Ltd.
1104 Franklin St.
Vancouver, British Columbia
V6A 106
(metal detectors, dredges,
supplies)

Garrett Electronics, Inc.
2814 National Drive
Garland, Texas 75041
(metal detectors, Garrett Gravity Trap gold pans)

Gold Genie World Wide
P.O. Box 322
Canyonville, Oregon 97417
(wheel-type concentrator)

Gold Grabber Mfg. Co.
P.O. Box 3255
Boise, Idaho 83707
(small-scale mining equipment,
supplies)

Gold-Vac
Western Sports
3725 South Stone
Spokane, Washington 99203
(suction dredges)

Keene Engineering, Inc.
Dept. WT
9330 Corbin Ave.
Northridge, California 91324
(sluices, pumps, dredges, con-
centrators, diving equipment,
books)

Mighty-Lite
318 Wrex Ct.
Chico, California 95926
(dredges, winches, crushers)

Miner's Incorporated
P.O. Box 1301
Riggins, Idaho 83549
(prospecting equipment,
supplies)

Rocky Mountain Detectors Ltd.
P.O. Box 5366
Postal Stn. "A"
Calgary, Alberta T2H 1X8
(metal detectors, dredges,
supplies)

Treasure Emporium
12823 Foothills Blvd.
Sylmar, California 91342
(small-scale mining equipment,
dredges, supplies)

A Glossary of Prospecting and Mining Terms

The following list contains some of the special language encountered in this book and in other references on the subject. Defined here in terms of their application to placer mining, some of these words have entirely different meanings in other fields.

Abandonment The act of relinquishing title to a claim or prospecting lease, either voluntarily or by failure to perform assessment work.

Above Accompanied by a number, denotes a claim upstream from the original or "discovery" claim.

Adit More or less horizontal passage made into the earth for mining or drainage purposes; open at one end.

Air shaft Shaft used to ventilate a mining draft.

Alloy Mixture of metals, often man-made to improve certain qualities: for example, adding silver to gold to make it harder. Brass is an *alloy* of copper and zinc.

Alluvial Associated with sand or clay gradually deposited by moving water. Placer deposits are often *alluvial* in nature. An alluvial fan is a wide area where the stream has slowed down: a river delta.

Amalgam The fusing of mercury and gold.

Amalgamation Recovery of gold from concentrates by use of mercury.

Amorphous Lacking a definite crystalline form.

Andesite Fine-grained volcanic rock.

Apron The part of the rocker stretched on a frame beneath the hopper that traps fine particles of gold as they fall through the screen.

Aqua regia Mixture of one part nitric acid to three parts hydrochloric acid; will dissolve gold and platinum.

Argillite Hardened mudstone showing no slatelike cleavage.

Assay Quantitative analysis of metals present in a sample expressed in percentage or dollar value.

Assessment work The annual labor which must by law be performed to hold a claim.

Auriferous Containing gold.

Bar Projection of gravel or sand into a stream, above or below the water line.

Barren Ground that contains no gold or valuable minerals.

Base line Line, carefully surveyed, from which other points are measured.

Base metals Industrial metals such as copper, lead, tin, and so on, as opposed to precious or noble metals such as gold, silver and platinum.

Bedrock Solid rock overlain by unconsolidated material.

Bedrock drain Trench dug downstream from an open cut to facilitate the drainage of water from the diggings.

Below Accompanied by a number, it designates a claim which is downstream from the original discovery claim.

Bench Former stream bed, now a flat area above the present stream bed.

Bench placer Placer deposit contained in a bench.

Black sand The major, visible portion of pan concentrates: composed of magnetite, hematite or other heavy minerals. Settles faster than ordinary sand much the same way as gold does, and is a good indicator of placer gold.

Bonanza Extremely rich mining creek or vein.

Booming The storing up and sudden release of water in placer mining.

Bullion Melted but unrefined gold or silver.

Burn down To sink a shaft in frozen ground by thawing with fire.

Carat Metric unit for weighing precious stones, equal to 200 milligrams; sometimes used interchangeably with karat (see below).

Cemented gravel Hard, tightly packed yet unconsolidated layer of gravel; can form a false bedrock.

Cenozoic The latest era in geological time; begins about 65,000,000 years ago.

Chert Very fine-grained rock occurring in limestone beds.

Claim Parcel of land granted for mining purposes.

Clastic Consisting of fragments of older rocks.

Claim jumper One who illegally stakes or works a claim belonging to another.

Clean-up Collecting the valuable products from a sluice or mill.

Coarse gold Gold fragments and nuggets too large to pass through a 10-mesh screen.

Colors Pieces of gold smaller than a nugget – may be particles, specks or dust. In test panning, the more colors, and the larger they are, the better the prospect.

Concentrates The residue left in the rocker, pan or sluice box after a quantity of gravel has been washed; usually composed of black sand and precious metals.

Conglomerate Gravels which have been cemented together in a natural process.

Core drill A drill which will remove below-surface samples from solid rock. The samples take the form of cylindrical *cores* brought up by the drill.

Country rock The normal rock or rocks surrounding a mineral deposit; also called host rock.

Crevice Split or fissure in bedrock; often traps placer gold.

Cribbing Close timbering used to line a shaft.

118

Dendritic Branching tree-like pattern.

Deposit Area where gold is found. There are two types of placer deposits – eluvial (near the originating rock) and alluvial (found a considerable distance away because of being waterborne).

Detritus Chips, fragments, and grains of minerals or rocks, resulting from disintegration by weathering.

Discovery The first valuable minerals found by a prospector that would warrant further prospecting and testing.

Discovery claim On placer creeks, the first claim recorded on a creek, or the first claim staked after all others had lapsed. In the Yukon this claim can be three times the length of a standard creek claim.

Drain Trench or adit to drain placer diggings.

Dredge Machine for scooping or sucking gravel from a river or creek.

Drift Boulder, till, gravel, sand and clay deposited by a glacier, or by streams formed by a melting glacier. Also a horizontal underground passage, leading off from a shaft.

Drifting The digging out of a horizontal passage underground.

Ductile Capacity of metals to be drawn out into fine wires without breaking.

Dust Fine particles of gold; called *flour gold* today.

Easement Right-of-way across another person's property or claim, for which no compensation is paid.

Eldorado Name frequently used to describe an unusually rich mineral claim or creek. Origin: Spanish legendary land of gold and plenty, "the golden place."

Electrum Natural alloy of gold and silver.

Element Chemical substance that cannot be changed into any other substance by ordinary chemical means. Gold is an element.

Eluvial Refers to the weathering of rocks in place.

Eluvial placers Detrital minerals concentrated near a vein or outcrop, deposited there by gravity or rainwater.

Enigmatical Perplexing; of unknown origin.

Erosion The process by which rocks are broken down and transported; includes weathering, solution and corrosion.

Ferrous Containing iron.

Fineness Measure of the purity of gold.

Float Loose fragments that have been separated from a mineral deposit.

Flour gold The most used term today for gold in very fine, powdery form – the "dust" of old-time parlance.

Flume Sloping waterway, usually a ditch, used to transport water.

Foliation Laminated rock structure resulting from the alignment of different minerals into parallel layers; characteristic of schists and micas.

Fool's gold Any material that looks enough like gold to be taken by neophytes for the real thing. Examples are pyrite and mica.

Fraction Area lying between two claims that is less than the full size of a normal claim. Usually results from an error in measurement by the original stakers.

Geochemical prospecting The analysis of rocks, silts, soils, spring waters, surface waters and organisms for abnormal concentrations of elements.

Gneiss Coarsely crystal-grained rock banded with minerals such as mica and quartz. Pronounced "nice."

Gradient The dip or slope of a stream or sluice box.

Grains In troy measurement, the small weights used to balance against gold. Twenty-four grains = one pennyweight; 20 pwt = 1 ounce.

Granite Very hard crystalline rock, gray to pink in color.

Grizzly Screen or grating used to keep rocks and boulders out of a sluice box.

Ground sluicing Using the natural force of diverted stream water to wash away overburden.

Hardpan Layer of hardened clay or cemented gravel.

Hardrock Term used to describe a lode or mineral vein that is enclosed in solid rock.

Hematite Iron oxide with a reddish-brown streak.

Hidden values In placer mining, particles of gold too small to be seen with the naked eye. It's wise to check for these after the visible gold has been removed from concentrates.

Hydraulic mining, hydraulicking Using water under great pressure to wash away overburden or bring down hillside banks of gravel; or to flush them through sluices.

Ice bridge Road across a frozen river.

Igneous Rock formed by hardening of molten materials (magma) deep within the earth.

Ingot Metal bar of silver or gold cast in a convenient size for handling or measuring.

Intrusive Molten body of rock that was forced into or between other rocks, then cooled and hardened. (Volcanic rocks, on the other hand, are *extrusive*.)

Ironstone Sedimentary rock having a high percentage of iron; often occurs with gold placers, and an indicator every prospector looks for.

Jig Screen in which concentrates are further washed and sorted by shaking them in water.

Kame Conical hill or short ridge of gravel and sand deposited by a glacier.

Karat One twenty-fourth part of gold in alloys. Twenty-four karat (24 k) gold is pure gold.

Lava Fluid rock issuing from a volcano or fissure; also used to describe rocks formed from this material.
Lay Working agreement under which a miner leases staked ground in return for giving a percentage of what he finds to the owner.
Limit The bank of a stream looking downstream; that is, left limit or right limit.
Locate The act of staking or fixing the boundaries of a claim.
Lode Deposit of metallic ore in solid, consolidated rock; an abundant or rich source, from which placer gold is thought to have come.
Long tom Sluicing system consisting of a puddling box, screen, and sluice box.
Luster The light-reflecting quality of a mineral.

Magma Liquid rock deep in the earth; hardens to from igneous rock.
Magnetite Magnetic black iron oxide. Also known as lodestone and as black sand.
Malleable Describes metal that can be hammered or flattened without breaking.
Mercury Heavy, liquid metal with a very low melting and vaporizing point; also called quicksilver.
Mesh The size of openings in a sieve or screen.
Metamorphic rock Rocks which have been altered by changes in temperature, pressure and chemical action.
Mica One of a group of minerals that crystallize in thin, flexible, easily separated layers.
Mineral Natually occurring, inorganic element or compound with a definite chemical composition and a characteristic external structure.
Monitor Giant nozzle or jet through which water is forced at high pressure in hydraulic mining.
Moraine Accumulation of rocks and dirt, carried and deposited in a mass by a glacier.
Mother lode Principal vein system of metallic ore; the lode from which a placer deposit originated.
Muskeg Swamp or bog.

Nitric acid Corrosive liquid with very poisonous vapors; diluted with water to clean gold concentrates.
Noble metals Metals that react very little to chemicals, ordinary acids, air: especially gold and platinum.
Non-ferrous Mineral with no iron content.
Novice Amateur or beginner; an inexperienced prospector or miner.
Nugget Lump of native gold (or silver, copper, platinum).

Octahedral Having eight plane surfaces.

Old channel Ancient streambed left by a waterway that changed course.

Open cut Also called open pit; a surface mining operation.

Ore Mixture of one or more minerals forming a deposit that could be mined at a profit.

Outcrop The point where a mineral deposit is exposed above the earth's surface.

Outside Anywhere outside the boundaries of the Yukon Territory.

Overburden Poor-paying or barren surface soil, clay or gravel covering a valuable mineral deposit; the material must be penetrated to get to the paydirt.

Paydirt Earth, rocks, sand, or gravels which can be mined for a profit.

Paystreak The layer of a gold-bearing stream's gravel in which high gold values are obtained; the richest part of a placer.

Pennyweight Unit used to weigh gold. Twenty pennyweights are equal to one troy ounce.

Permafrost Overburden (soil or gravel) that is frozen all year round.

Placer Mass of sand or gravel containing recoverable particles of gold or other minerals.

Pleistocene The epoch of the Cenozoic era of geological time when the most recent Ice Age occurred.

Pocket Deposit with heavy concentration of gold, often in a crevice or under a rock. Sometimes denotes a rich part of a claim missed by the old-timers.

Poke Moosehide or leather bag for carrying placer gold.

Pothole Cavity in bedrock formed by the action of stones in a whirlpool or eddy of a stream; usually does not contain a placer.

Precipitate The solid produced when one solution is added to another; also to cause such a precipitate to form.

Prospect Unproven but promising mineral discovery; to search for mineral deposits.

Puddling box Box (at the top of a sluice) in which hardened clay or cemented gravels are broken up.

Pup Short creek, tributary to another.

Quartz Crystallized silicone dioxide. One of the most common minerals associated with gold deposits.

Quartz mining Same as hardrock mining.

Quicksilver Mercury (see above).

Raise Mine shaft worked upward from a drift.

Recent As an expression of geological time, refers to the current epoch; also used to describe deposits formed since the Ice Age.

Refine To purify crude metals, removing dross, sediments, alloyed metals.

122

Retort Apparatus with which to recover mercury after it has been used to amalgamate gold.

Riffles Obstructions built into the bottom of a sluice box to create turbulence and trap gold particles.

Rocker Device used to capture fine gold.

Royalty Percentage of gold value, paid by the miner to the Crown.

Rusty gold Free gold that is coated with iron or other minerals.

Schist Crystalline metamorphic rock that can easily be split along planes of foliation.

Sedimentary rock Rock formed by the deposition of sediments under water or on land; cemented sediments.

Sediments Unconsolidated rock forming material, commonly deposited in layers by wind or water.

Seismic Pertaining to the study of shock or sound waves.

Silica Hard, glassy mineral found in such forms as quartz and sand.

Shaft Narrow downward excavation of the earth.

Shaking table Inclined table with riffles, which is shaken to concentrate ore.

Sluice box Inclined trough with riffles in its bottom to trap heavy minerals.

Sluicing The process of washing gravels.

Sourdough Old-timer; one who has passed a winter in the Yukon; also, fermented biscuit dough. (A local definition: Somebody who is sour on the country, but has no dough to leave.)

Stake To mark out the limits of a claim; also a quantity of capital that enables one to start a new venture.

Striations Parallel lines marking the surface of bedrock or boulders.

Stripping The removal of overburden in sheet-like sections, rather than by digging trenches or shafts.

Tailings Waste material left after the valuable minerals have been removed from ore or gravel; overburden that has been removed and piled up or transported.

Talus The slide rock at the bottom of a slope.

Tertiary The earlier of the two periods comprising the Cenozoic era of geological time.

Till Loose, unsorted glacial material.

Trommel Large, revolving sieve.

Troy weights System of measurement used for precious metals.

Tunnel Underground passage, open at both ends.

Unconsolidated deposits Material in loose form, not converted to solid rock: sand, gravel, placers, clay, detritus.

Undercurrent Current of water flowing under the surface of the main current in a sluice box, sometimes in a different direction.

Values The relative amounts of precious and other metals found in sample rock or placer gravels.
Vein Mineral deposit that is longer than it is wide, usually lying in fissures. Also called a lode.

Water table The top limit of water saturation in the layer of unconsolidated earth or gravel above bedrock.
Weathering Physical or chemical changes caused by the exposure of rocks to wind, water, sunlight, freezing, and so on.
Wet ground Unfrozen ground below the water table.
Wet hole Shaft that encounters water.
Wing dam Dam built on an angle so as to direct a stream in the desired way; often used in ground sluicing.

Recommended Reading

Anthony, Leo Mark. *Introductory Prospecting and Mining*. University of Alaska, 1982.
Berton, Pierre. *Klondike*. McClelland and Stewart Limited, 1972.
Boericke, William F. *Prospecting and Operating Small Gold Placers*. John Wiley & Sons, 1936.
Bostock, H.S. *Yukon Territory: Selected Field Reports of the Geological Survey of Canada, 1898 to 1933, Memoir 284*. Supply and Services Canada, 1957.
Bostock, H.S. *Glaciation, Central Yukon Territory, Paper 65,36*. Geological Survey of Canada, 1966.
Boyle, R.W. *The Geochemistry of Gold and Its Deposits*. Supply and Services Canada, 1979.

Canadian Permanent Committee on Geographic Names. *Gazetteer of Canada: Yukon Territory*. Supply and Services Canada, 1981.
Debicki, R.L. *Yukon Mineral Industry, 1941 to 1959*. Supply and Services Canada, 1983.
Debicki, R.L. *Yukon Placer Mining Industry, 1978-82*. Supply and Services Canada, 1983.
Enan, D.S., Downing, D.A., and Morin, J.A. *1984 Yukon Mining and Exploration Overview*. Department of Indian Affairs and Northern Development Exploration and Geological Surveys Division, Whitehorse, 1985.
Gardner, E.D., Johnson, C.H. *Placer Mining in the Western*

United States, Parts 1, 2 and 3. Information Circular, Department of the Interior, United States Bureau of Mines, 1934, 1935. Reprinted by Exanimo Press (Gazette Publications), 1971, under the title: *Placer Miners' Manual*, Volumes 1, 2 and 3, by Karl von Mueller.

Gilbert, G.W. *Yukon Placer Mining*. Booklet, Supply and Services Canada, 1981.

Gilbert, G.W. *A Brief History of Placer Mining in the Yukon*. Supply and Services Canada, 1983.

Hurlbut, Cornelius S. Jr., and Klein, Cornelius. *Manual of Mineralogy*. John Wiley & Sons, Inc., 1977.

Indian and Northern Affairs Canada. *Yukon Geology and Exploration 1979-80*. Supply and Services Canada, 1981.

Indian and Northern Affairs Canada. *Yukon Exploration and Geology, 1981*. Supply and Services Canada, 1982.

Indian and Northern Affairs Canada. *Yukon Exploration and Geology, 1982*. Supply and Services Canada, 1983

Lang, A.H. *Prospecting in Canada*. Supply and Services Canada, 1970.

McCracken, David *Advanced Dredging Techniques, Professional Gold Dredger's Handbook*. Keene Industries, 1081.

Pearl, Richard M. *Handbook For Prospectors*. McGraw-Hill, 1973.

Pough, Frederick H. *A Field Guide to Rocks and Minerals*. Houghton Mifflin Company, 1976.

U.S. Bureau of Mines. *Information Circular # 6786* .

U.S. Department of the Interior. *Placer Examination, Principles and Practice*, Technical Bulletin 4, Bureau of Land Management.

Western and Eastern Treasures Magazine. *Silver & Gold Issue*, 1982.

Wolff, Ernest. *Handbook for the Alaskan Prospector*. University of Alaska, 1969.

Note: Government publications still in print are available by mail from The Canadian Government Publishing Centre, Supply and Services Canada, Ottawa, Ontario K1A 0S9.

A

abandonment, *def* 117
above, *def* 117
Adams Creek, 89, 100
adit, 50
aerial photographs, 113
aeronautical maps, 112
Agate Creek, 100
air shaft, *def* 117
Aishihik Lake, 97
Alaska, viii, 84, 85, 99
Alaska Highway, viii, 45
Alberta Creek, 100
Alder Creek, 100
Allgold Creek, 87, 89, 90, 100
alloy, *def* 10
alluvial, *def* 117
amalgamate, *def* 75
Anderson Creek, 100
andesite, *def* 117
apron, *def* 117
Arch Creek, 90, 91
area of Yukon, viii
argillite, *def* 117
assaying, 74
assessment work, *def* 117; 59, 64

B

Back Creek, 100
Ballarat Creek, 100
bar mining, 36, 54, 56
Barker Creek, 98, 99, 100
Barlow Creek, 100
base line, *def* 117
base metals, *def* 117
Bear Creek, 87, 90, 101
Beaufort Sea, vii
Beaver River, 93
bedrock, *def* 117
Bedrock Creek, 100
Beliveau Creek, 100
Beloud Creek, 100
below, *def* 118
bench, *def* 118
bench placers, *def* 118; 19, 54
Big Creek, 99, 100
Big Gold Creek, 101
Big Salmon River, 56
Bismarck Creek, 101
Black Hills Creek, 101
black sand, *def* 118; 36, 57, 74, 76
blasting permits, 113

blue clay, 47
Blueberry Creek, 101
Bonanza Creek, 13, 25, 27, 45, 84, 87, 88, 89, 101
Borden Creek, 101
books on mining, 112, 124
booming, 47
Bostock, H.S., 1932 Report, 99
Bostock Report, The, 28, 33, 50, 79, 100
Boucher Creek, 101
Boulder Creek, 89, 101
Brewer Creek, 101
Brittania Creek, 101
bullion, *def* 118
Bullion Creek, 90, 91, 101
Burwash Creek, 90, 91

C

Cabin Creek, 101
Cairns, D.D., 1915 Report, 97
Caledonia Creek, 29
California Creek, 85, 101
California gold rush, 16, 54
Campbell Creek, 95, 96
Canada Creek, 90
Canadian Creek, 101
Canadian Shield, 17
carat, *def* 118
Cariboo Crossing, 90
Caribou Creek, 101
Carmack, George, 87
Carmack River, 97
Carmacks District, 99
Cascade Creek, 101
Casino Creek, 101
Cassiar Bar, 56
Cassiar gold fields, 95
cassiterite, 74
cemented gravel, *def* 118
chamois, use of, 75
chalcopyrite, 9
chemical prospecting methods, 57
Christal Creek, 101
churn drills, 49
citizenship requirements, viii, 60
claims, *def* 105, 118; assessment work required, 63; buying, 61; renewal dates, 60; fees required, 110; how to measure, 105; staking, 36, 46, 60, 105; claim jumping, viii, 46; leases on, 62, 108; numbering posts, 107;

recording, 107; re-staking, 60; restrictions on locating, 105; right to acquire, 105; size, 106; transfers, 110; foreign ownership, viii
Clarke Creek, 101
Clear Creek, 92, 101
coarse gold, 16
colors, *def* 46, 118; counting, 45
concentrator, wheel type, 115
Congdon Creek, 93
conglomerate, *def* 18, 118
copper, 7, 10
Cottoneva Creek, 83, 99, 101
cribbing, 50, 118
crushers, 115
customs and excise, 112

D

dams, building, 47
Davis Creek, 85
Dawson, 2, 5, 30, 45, 84
Dawson Charlie, 90
Dawson City Public Library, 79
Dawson Daily News, 30
Dease Lake, 97
Deep Creek, 101
Department of Indian Affairs and Northern Development (DIAND), 79
deposits, *def* 119
DIAND, 79
diorite, 92
discovery claims, *def* 119
district map, 132
district mining recorders, 64, 76
diving equipment, 115
Dixie Creek, 90
Dolly Creek, 101
Dome Creek, 101
Dominion Creek, 52, 87, 88, 89, 101
Donjek River, 90, 91
dowsing, 38
drainage, 47
dredges, 20, 56, 115; *def* 119; bucket-line, 54
drift, *def* 119
drift mining, 25, 50, 53, 54
drifting, *def* 119
drilling, 49
Dublin Gulch, 101
Duncan Creek, 92, 101
Duncan mining district, 95, 96
dust, *def* 119

E

earth moving equipment, 52
easement, *def* 119
Edwards Creek, 93
Edmonton (Battleford) Creek, 101
effluent standards, 64
Eldorado, 13, 25, 27, 28, 88, 89, 101; *def* 119
Eliza Creek, 101
eluvial placers, *def* 119
environmental damage, 54
equipment sources, 115; importing, viii
erosion, 17, 20; *def* 119
Eureka Creek, 87, 89, 101

F

Falle, Al, 38
Ferguson Creek, 101
fineness, *def* 119; 10
Finlayson River, 102
fire assays, 46
Firth River, 101
Fivemile Creek, 101
Flat Creek, 87, 101
float, *def* 119
flour gold, 10; *def* 119
flume, 47; *def* 119
foliation, *def* 119
fool's gold, 8, 9; *def* 120
foreign claims, viii
Fortymile, 85
Fortymile River, 101
Fourth of July Creek, 90, 101
fraction, *def* 120
Frances River, 95
Frobisher, Martin, 8
frozen ground, working, 52, 54

G

gadgets, use in prospecting, 36
Galena Creek, 98
game management, 112
Garrett Gravity Trap pan, 42, 115
Gay Gulch, 89
Gazeteer of Canada: Yukon Territory, 32
geochemical prospecting, 38; *def* 120
geological maps, 32, 112
geology, where to write for information, 112

Geological Survey of Canada, 28, 33, 100
Gilbert, George, Claims Inspector, 33
Glacier Creek, 28, 85, 102
glaciers, 20-25, 53, 54, 98
Gladstone Creek, 90
gneiss, def 120
gold, alloys, 7, 8; average value, 50; buying and selling, 76; coarse gold, def 16; chemical processes affecting, 8; selling concentrates, 76; conductor, 8; ductility, 8; element, 8; exporting, 76; fineness, 10; forms taken, 8; fool's, def 120; 8, 9; "growing" in streams, 27, 29; hardness, 9; jewelry quality, 10, 76; minerals confused with, 8; noble metal, 8; def 120; precious metal, 10; price, 79; properties, 8; raw gold, 8; recovery machines (general), 72; refining, 10; removing from concentrates, 74; royalty paid on, 76; def 123; rusty gold, def 123; 8; testing for gold, 9; untapped sources, 29
Gold Creek, 85
Gold Run Creek, 87, 89, 102
Gold Rush, 1, 7, 41, 59, 61, 64
goldbearing creeks and rivers of the Yukon, list, 100
Goldbottom Creek, 87, 102
gophering, 46
Goring Creek, 102
government reports, 33
grains, def 120
granite, def 120
Gravel (Keele) River, 95, 96
grizzly bears, 35, 57
grizzly, def 120; pan, 45
ground sluicing, 47, 48; def 120

H

Haggart Creek, 102
Hamilton Creek, 102
hardrock, def 120
hardrock mines, 15, 53, 62
Hayes Creek, 102
hematite, 17, 74; def 120
Henderson, Bob, 87
Henderson Creek, 84, 102
Hess River, 93
Hester Creek, 89, 102

hidden values, def 120
Highet Creek, 102
holding area, 47
Hoole River, 95
Hootalinqua, 56
Hunker Creek, 27, 87, 88, 89, 102
hydraulicking, 48, 54; def 120

I

ice bridge, def 120
igneous rock, def 120
ilmenite, 74
immigration, 112
importing equipment, viii
Indian River, 87, 102
information sources, 112
ingot, def 120
intrusive rock, def 120
Iron Creek, 99, 102
iron oxide, 8
ironstone, def 120

J

Jansen Creek, 89
Jarvis River, 102
jig, def 120
Johnson Creek, 98, 102

K

kame, def 120
karats, 10; def 121
Kennebec Creek, 29
Kenyon Creek, 27
Keystone Creek, 102
Kimberley Creek, 90
King Solomon's Dome, 25
Kirkman Creek, 98, 102
Klondike, 1, 7, 13, 25, 27, 61, 82, 84, 85, 87, 88, 98, 99; River, 20, 87, 102; Visitor's Association, 5, 45
Kluane Lake, 90
Kluane Mining District, 90
Koidern River, 102

L

Ladue River, 93
Lake Creek, 83, 92, 99, 102
land use, 63, 112
Lansing River, 93

overburden, 47, 49; *def* 122

P

Pan Creek, 103
panning, how to, 42
pans, 42; Garrett Gravity Trap, 42,
    115; grizzly, 45; plastic, 42, 75; steel,
    42; mechanical, 56
Parent Creek, 103
paydirt, 45; *def* 122
paystreak, 18; *def* 122
Peel River, 92
Pelly River, 92, 95, 96, 103
pennyweight, *def* 122
permafrost, 47, 50; *def* 122
photographs, aerial, 25, 36; satellite, 36
placers, *def* 15, 122; and glaciers, 23;
    gravel-plain placers, 20; how formed,
    16; classification of placer gold, 16;
    patterns of placer deposits, 18; types
    of placer deposits, 20
Placer Mining Act, The, 60, 64;
    excerpts 105
Placer Mining Times, The, 30, 36
platinum, 17, 74
pleistocene, *def* 122
pocket, *def* 122
poke, *def* 122
Poker Creek, 85, 103
Portland Creek, 103
pothole, *def* 122
Preacher Creek, 103
Precambrian, 17, 98
precipitate, *def* 122
Prevost Canyon, 96
Primrose Creek, 103
prospect, *def* 122
proven ground, 62
puddling box, *def* 122
pup, *def* 122
pyrites, 8, 9

Q

quartz, *def* 122; 15
Quartz Creek, 87, 89, 90
quartz mining, *def* 122
quicksilver, *def* 122
Queenstake Resources, 27
Quiet Lake, 99
Quill Creek, 91

R

Rackla River, 93
raise, *def* 122
refine, *def* 122
reports by private mining companies, 33
retort, *def* 122
research, 30, 36
Rice Creek, 103
riffles, 67; *def* 123; Hungarian, 68
road maps, 112
Roaring Fork Creek, 103
rockers, 56, 67, 72; *def* 123
Rosebud Creek, 103
Ross River, 56, 95, 96
RCMP, 57; files as information source,
    100
royalty, *def* 123; 76
Ruby Range, 90
Ruby Creek, 90
Rupe Creek, 93
Rusk Creek, 103
rusty gold, *def* 123

S

St. Elias Mountain Range, 21, 90
St. Germain Creek, 83
Salmon River, 81
Sayyea Creek, 103
schist, *def* 123
Scroggie Creek, 98, 103
Scurvey Creek, 103
season for mining activity, viii
sedimentary rock, *def* 123
sediments, *def* 123
Selwyn River, 103
Service, Robert, 5
settling ponds, 47, 72
Seven Pup Creek, 27
Seymour Creek, 99, 103
shaft, *def* 123
shaft sinking, 50
shaking table, *def* 123
Sheep Creek, 90, 103
Shootanook Creek, 103
Shorty Creek, 103
Sidney Creek, 104
silver, 7, 10, 17
Silver Creek, 104
Sixtymile, 81, 84, 85
Sixtymile River, 104
Slate Creek, 104
Slims River, 90

sluice boxes, 67, 68, 115; *def* 123;
    cleaning, 70; commercial versions,
    67; Flying Dutchman, 38; triple
    sluice, 54, 56; ground sluicing, 47,
    48; *def* 120
Snyder Creek, 90
sources of equipment, 115
sourdough, *def* 123
Southwestern Yukon, 97
Spanish dip needle, 36
specific gravity, 9
speculators, 60, 62
Squaw Creek, 104
stake, *def* 123
Steamboat Bar, 36, 56
Steele River, 104
Steep Creek, 104
Stewart River, 20, 36, 56, 84, 92, 93,
    98, 104
Stoddard Creek, 99, 104
striations, *def* 123
strip mining technique, 52, 123
suction dredges, 47, 54
Sulphur Creek, 87, 89, 104
Summit Creek, 83, 99, 104
supplies, sources, 115
Swede Creek, 104
Sydney Creek, 99
Sylvia Creek, 81, 83

T

Tagish Creek, 104
tailings, dumping, 63; *def* 123
talus, *def* 123
Tatamagouche Creek, 91, 104
Telluride Creek, 90
Tempelman-Kluit, Dirk, 28, 29
Tenmile Creek, 104
Teraktu Creek, 104
tertiary, *def* 123
Teslin River, 56, 81, 104
test pitting, 46
thawing frozen ground, 52
Thistle Creek, 83, 84, 98, 99, 104
till *def* 123
timbering, 53
topographical maps, 33, 112
travel in Yukon, 35, 57
trommel, *def* 121
Troy weights, 10; *def* 123
tuffs, 92
Twelfth of July Creek, 104

Twelvemile Creek, 85, 104

U

Unconsolidated deposits, *def* 123
Upper Liard River, 95
Upper Liard River Region, 92

V

values, *def* 124
veins, 17; *def* 124
Venturi principle, 54
Victoria Creek, 97
Victoria Gulch, 27, 88, 89
virgin ground, 62
Vulcan Creek, 90

W

Walhalla Creek, 104
washing gravels, 67
water licenses, 63
water rights, 113
water storage ponds, 47
water table, *def* 124
water use, 63
weathering, 17; *def* 124
Webber Creek, 104
weedeater, 36
White River, 29, 83, 90
Whitehorse, 3, 29, 45, 79, 104
Williams Creek, 104
winches, 115
wing dam, *def* 124
witching, 38

Y

Yukon Archives, 33, 79, 100
Yukon Geology Office, 33
Yukon Government, Wildlife Branch,
    57
The Yukon Placer Mining Act, 60, 64;
    excerpts, 105
Yukon River, 56, 81, 83, 84, 87, 92, 96,
    98

Z

Zinc Creek, 104

Mining Districts
of the Yukon

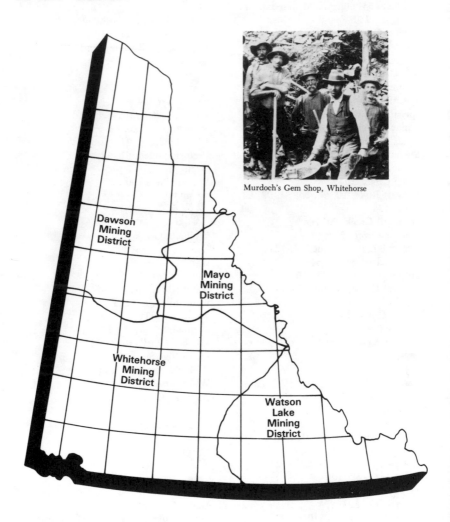

Murdoch's Gem Shop, Whitehorse

Dawson
Mining
District

Mayo
Mining
District

Whitehorse
Mining
District

Watson
Lake
Mining
District

The basics: shovel, pan, pick, grizzly.

Mike Laforet

Black Mike instructing a beginner

133

Other titles from
Outcrop
The Northern Publishers
Box 1350
Yellowknife, Northwest Territories,
Canada X1A 2N9

Great Bear: A Journey Remembered
Frederick B. Watt

Plant Magic for Northern Gardens
Chriss D. Briggs

On Blue Ice: The Inuvik Adventure
Jane Stoneman-McNichol, ed.

Rebels, Rascals and Royalty:
The Colourful North of LACO Hunt
Barbara Hunt, ed.

Christmas In the Big Igloo:
True Tales from the Canadian Arctic
Kenn Harper, ed.

Yellowknife
Carolyn Czarnecki/Hans O. Barfod

Harvesting the Northern Wild
Marilyn Walker